Raising the Bar
on
Service Excellence

The Health Care Leader's Guide
to Putting Passion into Practice

By Kristin Baird, RN, BSN, MHA

Golden Lamp Press

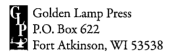 Golden Lamp Press
P.O. Box 622
Fort Atkinson, WI 53538

This is a non-fiction publication. Patient names have been changed to protect confidentiality. Hospital or organization names may have been omitted for confidentiality upon request of the interviewee or by discretion of the author.

Ordering Information
To order additional copies, call (920) 563-4684 or log onto
www.baird-consulting.com. Quantity discounts are available.
ISBN 978-0-9754733-4-4 (paperback)

Baird, Kristin M., 1957-
     Raising the Bar on Service Excellence; The Health Care Leader's Guide to Putting Passion into Practice   / Kristin M. Baird
     ISBN 978-0-9754733-4-4
     1. Health Care Management   2. Health Care Leadership
     3. Patient Satisfaction   4. Baird, Kristin

Credits
     Editor: Teresa Peneguy Paprock
     Cover Design: Mark Dziewior

First printing: July 2008 (paperback)

Acknowledgments

No real accomplishments in life happen without support. In life and in business, I have been infinitely blessed with people who have encouraged me, taught me, supported me, challenged me, picked me up when I fell flat and rejoiced with me over successes large and small. There are really too many to mention here, so I will limit the list to those who were directly involved in this book. For those who I don't mention by name; hopefully you know who you are. Please know how grateful I am for your love and support.

I want to thank Kevin Stranberg who has been my right hand in consulting for the past four years. Your friendship and support mean the world to me. Gretchen Olsen, my sister and executive assistant has been my lifesaver. Thanks for keeping my life in order. To my editor, Teresa Peneguy Paprock. Thanks for making the tight deadlines. To Audrey Fixmer, Rob Fixmer, and Bridget Nsibirwa who not only edited this book, but in the process, helped me to grow as a writer. Thank you for sharing your skills and helping me to improve mine. Mom and Rob, forgive me for not acquiring the grammar and punctuation gene. I'm still learning.

To Quint Studer for being a mentor in my early career and for writing the foreword.

My network of colleagues helped me find the great stories and people that enriched this book. So many people shared their successes and lessons to deepen the content of this book with their stories. The following pages are filled with your wisdom.

And finally, I thank my husband and designer Mark Dziewior. Your love and support are everything to me. Thank you for taking my words and making them beautiful. Your encouragement makes me believe in myself. Your artistic skills make my ideas a reality in print. Even though you are a skilled painter and sculptor, you still step up to help me at every turn. I am blessed to have you in my life.

Table of Contents

Foreword   *vi*

Introduction   *xi-xix*

Chapter 1: Priority   *1-55*

Chapter 2: People   *57-112*

Chapter 3: Processes   *113-149*

Chapter 4: Purpose   *151-173*

Chapter 5: Passion   *175-199*

Conclusion   *200*

Index   *201-203*

Foreword

In early civilization, fire was essential to life. People used fires to keep warm, cook food, light the way in darkness, and protect themselves from enemies. Without fire, people would perish.

Within each village, there were people whose primary job was to keep the fire burning. They tended to the fires themselves. But they also knew that one day the job would need to be done by someone else. So they taught others how to carry on the practice of keeping the flame burning, which allowed villages to prosper and grow, for years and years to come.

Today, the places where people spend the most time during their days are no longer their villages. It is their workplaces. But just like villages of old, the modern workplace still needs fire starters. Why? Because sometimes we lose our way and need to find the light again. The fire starters in our workplaces help rekindle our flame, our passion, and reconnect us to why we do what we do.

Healthcare organizations are no different. As I travel the country, I meet nurses who say they knew they wanted to be a nurse when they were six years old. They entered the profession at 22, eager to make a difference in the lives of patients and their families. But some of them got discouraged as their careers advanced. Sometimes they find themselves needing a fire starter to help rekindle their passion, that same passion that they had when they were six and 22. It's still there; they just haven't tapped into it in a while. I have met doctors with similar stories, as well as CEO's, respiratory therapists and housekeepers.

Kristin is a modern day fire starter. I have always been impressed by her passion and caring. Having worked with her and having followed her career over the years, it is clear that she has a long-term commitment to making healthcare better. It is wonderful that she has taken the time to compile the practical tips and stories of success that she has gathered over the years into this book. I think it will help reignite some fires, maybe yours.

-- Quint Studer
   Founder & CEO, Studer Group

About the Author

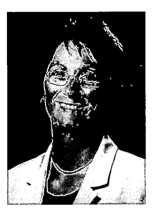

Kristin Baird is a highly sought after healthcare consultant and speaker. Baird's passion and perspective are based on thirty years of healthcare expertise, ranging from clinical nursing, to marketing and hospital administration.

Baird provides her health care clients with innovative service strategies, mystery shopping and employee engagement techniques. Baird is a widely published author and renowned industry speaker. Her passion for excellence is demonstrated through various articles and books, including "Customer Service in Healthcare – a Grassroots Approach to Creating a Culture of Service Excellence" and "Reclaiming the Passion- Stories that Celebrate the Essence of Nursing".

Baird earned a Bachelor of Science degree in nursing from the University of Wisconsin–Madison and a Master of Science degree in Health Services Administration from Cardinal Stritch University in Milwaukee, Wisconsin.

Introduction

Where did all the patients go? When were they replaced with savvy, well-informed consumers with high expectations of their health care providers?

Alas, life used to be so easy when we health care leaders knew for certain that we were in charge of health care. When we could tell the patients how things were going to be. When we could design services and processes for both our convenience and the physicians' preferences.

Today, however, we are operating in an era of consumer-driven health care. Transparency and consumer demand are forcing us to deliver our services in new and different ways. This shift requires a set of well-developed leadership skills that will elevate our organizations to a new level - one more patient-centric than provider-centric. For most health care organizations, this requires a culture shift directed by talented, multifaceted leaders.

Experience has shown that there is an art and a science involved in the process of shifting organizational culture. The science of a culture shift involves having the right people, processes and priorities in place. The art of culture-shifting requires passionate leadership and the ability to engage people at all levels of the organization.

Some might say that it is the passion, above all else, that determines a leader's ability to impact the culture. I'll never discount the importance of a leader's passion, but passion alone cannot possibly transform the culture. Passion must be coupled with each of four other essential elements in order to become more than a state of mind or one person's dream. First, a passionate leader must be able to clearly articulate priorities that align the organization on a clear path toward goals. Second, with priorities established, the passionate leader must have the right people doing the right things in order to move the organization forward in pursuit of the prioritized goals. The third essential is to have processes and systems in place that will support the people in order to maximize their efforts. And finally, a passionate leader will have the ability to help each individual define and foster a sense of purpose that furthers the goals of the organization.

When combined with people, priorities, and purpose, a passionate leader creates an unstoppable momentum that can transform entire organizations. And when the process allows that passion to be communicated from the top down (as well as the bottom up) in an organization, the results are amazing. Passionate leadership, combined with a grassroots approach to engaging the hearts and minds of all staff, is the secret to making significant changes.

This book is the result of a journey spanning the 30 years of my health care experience. It encompasses lessons learned at the bedside as well as those acquired in the executive suite. The one resounding lesson I have learned through the years is that a culture of service excellence requires persistence, insistence and consistence in order to move from good to great.

I think of the current era as the end of the Third Generation in customer service. The First Generation began in the late 1980s and early '90s. During this stage, health care leaders looked up one day and said, "Uh-oh, consumers expect us to serve them according to the same service standards held by other industries. How can that be? We are different. We are more sophisticated. We have powers to cure the sick and make the lame walk again."

During that First Generation, many health care leaders believed that this customer service fad would go away. Relatively few health care leaders saw our patients as active, informed consumers with a choice. At this phase many of us poured money into advertising to tell the world just how compassionate we were. Commercials filled the airwaves and printed materials poured into mailboxes (and, ultimately, landfills.) And, lo and behold, nothing really changed.

The Second Generation began in the late 1990s. In this period, health care organizations began actively measuring patient satisfaction. At first, many providers confused measuring satisfaction with actually taking action to change the patient experience. It took some time for us to figure out that simply measuring satisfaction wasn't going to change experience and ultimately raise satisfaction scores. But as the science of measuring patient satisfaction evolved, so did the providers' insight into what it would take to change the patient encounter. Once we understood that we had to change the way we did things in order to change the scores, many of us made significant changes in improving patient satisfaction, and the results were measurable if not palpable.

We are now at the end of the Third Generation, which began around 2001. During this period, we have invested in leadership development, staff training, and recognition. We have sought out best practices and learned from the stars. Many of us believed our organizations had finally "arrived." We breathed a sigh of relief that we could finally rest easy, knowing that our patients loved us. We have been doing the right things, and our satisfaction scores proved it. All was right with the world. But this time of self-congratulation was merely a blip on the radar screen as we begin to usher in another era.

Now we're stepping into the Fourth Generation, and our greatest challenge is to continue raising the bar. It's no longer acceptable to rest on the laurels of clinical quality, or to pat ourselves on the back for winning awards or hitting the 99th percentile in satisfaction. All of that can change in an instant if we don't have a strong foundation. HCAHPs, and social media such as patient blogs, are telling patients' stories publicly. Regardless of where you have been on the journey to service excellence, the consumer continues to raise the bar.

Now, clinical quality is simply a given. Today's consumers expect you to deliver competent services. What they want is a totally seamless experience anchored in trust. And we continue to fall short. The bottom line is this: You simply cannot implement your strategic plan if you don't have the culture to support it. That culture is about people doing the right things, at the right time, for the right reasons.

There is truth in the adage, "You never get a second chance to make a good first impression." Most of us accept the inherent truth in this statement. But when it comes to our patients' experience, we still leave so much up to chance. Some holdouts want to keep making excuses because, they say, health care is a unique field and therefore cannot be held to the same customer service standards as other industries.

It's true: health care is an unusual business. Just consider a few of the characteristics that differentiate our industry from others:

- Our customers are vulnerable and often in pain, physically and/or emotionally, when they present themselves to us. Knowing that our customers put their very lives in our hands is often a daunting - even humbling - experience for many health care professionals.

- Each customer group brings a vast range of expectations to its encounters with us. Consider the expectations of physicians compared to those of patients and employees. Each has a set of variables that influences their degree of satisfaction, engagement and, ultimately, loyalty. Some of these variables overlap, while some are important only to a single group. Either way, we have a responsibility to excel in all areas in order to recruit and retain the best talent and build a loyal customer base at the same time.

- Regulations and reimbursement are factors as well. In the health care field, we serve many masters in addition to the patient. Regulations have been put into place to ensure a prescribed standard for quality. While necessary, much of the associated documentation is laborious and time-consuming, and it places additional pressure on staff. The same person we expect to spend time with patients and be attentive at the bedside is also the source of data that must be entered into the computer, as the right documentation is needed for seamless communication and good clinical results, as well as for financial reimbursement.

Okay, we're different. That said, we need to stop playing the "we're different" card and start recognizing that consumers don't care about our workload or the regulations behind the scenes. They care about their experiences with us. It's time to raise the bar on service in health care. That means designing a predictably positive patient experience. And this won't happen by chance - it must happen by design.

Over-promising and under-delivering: A prescription for disaster

For years, marketers have created tag lines and brand identities promising consumers the best, friendliest, and most compassionate health care. Often disconnected from the end product, the brands were created for the advancement of business without engaging staff, and holding every employee accountable for living the brand promise. As we prepare to enter the Fourth Generation, organizations are becoming more aligned to living the promise. Engaged employees, standardized systems, and ongoing staff development help to maintain this necessary standard. Transparency in pricing and reporting are two additional elements that have raised the bar for health care. For the first time, through HCAHPs, hospitals will be rewarded financially for their transparency in reporting patients' opinions of their services.

I have spoken to representatives of hundreds of health care organizations across the country, and at times have asked them to call to mind companies best known for their stellar customer service. Predictably, Disney, Nordstrom, The Ritz-Carlton and Neiman Marcus frequent the list. But in the hundreds of times that I have asked this question, no one has ever mentioned a health care organization. How appalling! If service is at the very core of our business, why are we not among the best-of-the-best?

The very essence of our work is the ultimate human service. When people turn to us, they are at their most vulnerable. They are often frightened, under stress, and in need. During our encounters, these customers want nothing more than to be able to trust us with their very lives. When they cross the thresholds of our hospitals, clinics and long-term care facilities, they are placing their trust in us. How often do we meet or exceed their expectations? Even more importantly, how often do we disappoint them?

My hope for all of us who are striding confidently into the Fourth Generation of customer service is that we can make the changes necessary to earn the consumers' top-of-mind position for service excellence.

Patients don't just bring us their business. They honor us with their trust each time they engage in a provider/patient encounter. Building that trust is essential. It is an honor to care for our patients during their most vulnerable times. In order to raise the bar on service excellence, we need to create and foster a culture that engages every person in a unified mindset that makes patient trust a top priority.

Every time a patient comes into contact with a health care organization, he has dozens of moments of truth, deciding if we are who and what we say we are. Everything a patient sees, hears, feels and experiences while in our care should instill trust. This requires that we consciously take charge of the patient experience pathway, managing every moment of truth along it to create a predictably positive patient experience.

I have found that the health care leaders whose organizations are among the best in customer service share the "5 Ps" - five consistent principles in their leadership approach. These five principles are Priority, People, Process, Purpose and Passion. The remaining chapters explore the 5 Ps in more depth, but for the sake of an overview, the following is a synopsis of these principles:

Priority

The best leaders will not only recognize that service must be a top priority, they will be able to communicate that message and put enough energy and resources behind it to successfully gain a loyal following committed to the cause. Even though most leaders will tell me they set customer service as a top priority, there are relatively few organizations where I find that to be true. Making an occasional statement about priorities and actually living those priorities are two different things. Good intentions aren't enough. In Chapter One you will review some of the most important steps in establishing service as a true priority and putting specific actions into place that support that intention.

People

Successful organizations know that their work force, not the items that show up on the balance sheet, is their greatest asset. Leaders often claim this, but does the core of the organization really feel it? Hiring right, developing talent, and holding people accountable are among the common denominators found in the most successful organizations. But we often miss some of the most obvious opportunities for preserving the human asset in the work force. Chapter Two provides insight and tools for hiring and developing your work force into a high-performing, mission-driven and patient-centered team.

Processes

Are you who you say you are? Are the patient experiences consistent from day-to-day, person-to-person, and department-to-department? Successful organizations have mastered the art and the science of putting systems in place that create a predictably positive patient experience but give enough latitude so that employees can exercise some degree of discretion when problems arise. These systems standardize some of the most common situations and give structure to the service initiative itself. In Chapter Three, you will learn how to assess the patient experience pathway and determine where you might need to improve processes and systems in order to ensure a consistently positive patient experience.

Purpose

High-performing organizations have an engaged workforce in which each individual is crystal clear about how his or her role contributes to the mission and to the customer experience. Leaders who can help individuals form a strong connection to purpose will have one of the most essential elements in place. When each person feels that his or her contributions are for the good of the whole, the organization is more unified under a global purpose. Chapter Four gives examples of how to foster a sense of purpose among the members of your team and shares valuable insights from best practices.

Passion

There's another adage that states, "Love what you do and you will never work a day in your life." Although the subtitle of this book promises to help the reader to put passion into practice, I intentionally left the chapter on passion until the end. Leading with passion helps everyone to stay connected to the heart: the human side of health care services. The words "courage" and "encourage" have the same root meaning: heart. When I think of passionate leadership, I think of leadership that emanates from the heart. It takes courage to lead from the heart because passionate leaders put themselves "out there" every day, allowing themselves to be bit vulnerable by putting their hearts on the line. Passionate leaders also encourage others. They speak to others' hearts by encouraging them to be at their very best.

But passionate leadership alone is not enough. A leader can be passionate in his or her beliefs and in the quest for excellence, but without the other four fundamentals, will not have the tools necessary to raise the bar to the next level. It is only when the passionate leader can set priorities, foster efficient processes, and engage the grassroots, that he or she will see measurable and sustainable results. In addition to all of these essential traits, the health care leader must be committed to taking an honest look at himself and seting goals for personal development. For this reason, I have concluded each chapter with a series of questions for personal reflections along with some action steps to help set personal goals.

These are tough times in health care. But the path to a brighter future is paved with challenges. As leaders, we must rise to the challenges at hand and refortify ourselves with new tools and new strategies to strengthen the future of health care for our work force, our patients and ourselves.

Chapter One

"*There is nothing more difficult to carry out, nor more doubtful of success, nor more dangerous to handle than to initiate a new order of things.*"

- Niccolo Machiavelli

So a culture of service excellence is a priority in your organization. Is everyone on your team clear about that? Do they understand what is expected of them and how they are being evaluated according to organizational priorities? Do your communication strategies promote the priorities? Are the leaders living the example and holding everyone accountable for results?

This chapter will help you to understand how to make service excellence a priority throughout your organization, particularly in your leadership actions. Having a priority in your heart is one thing. But it takes some planning and conscious effort to keep that priority as a driving force for your daily actions, making it visible and exemplary so that others will follow.

Acting on your priorities means demonstrating your commitment to excellence at every turn. That can mean questioning the status quo and, at times, having to rethink the process and reallocate resources in order to stay the course.

Mixed messages

It is vital that you, as a leader, maintain clarity about priorities. Without clarity, you risk sending mixed messages and creating confusion and chaos.

For decades, budget has been king in health care. If you set out to serve that king as your No. 1 priority, the culture will surely reflect that value. A few years ago I was working in an organization where one of the managers was nothing short of a tyrant. She was known for being very harsh – borderline abusive with her staff. Her employee satisfaction scores were among the lowest, and her staff turnover rate the highest, in the organization. I had personally observed her berating an employee in front of his peers.

When I spoke with her vice president about my observations and voiced my concern that this manager's behavior wasn't conducive to the culture we were trying to promote, he said, "Yes, but she runs a tight ship." Not clear about what that meant, I probed a bit. He explained, "She stays within her budget, and that's what counts."

Well, if her boss was sending the message that budget was the highest priority, he was getting exactly the results he wanted. But in a mission-driven environment that places high value on service, fiscal performance must be kept in balance with other expectations, including customer service, employee engagement and quality.

"Money is a good servant but a bad master."

- Francis Bacon

Sending mixed messages about priorities can pose a real danger. It is one of the best creators of confusion I've seen. About three years ago, my colleagues and I were doing a culture assessment for a community hospital. During the management interviews, several of the managers complained that they were having trouble identifying their organization's highest priority. One manager said, "It seems like (the CEO) has a knee-jerk reaction to whatever the latest issue is. He'll call us together and say, 'This is a top priority,' and it will be totally unrelated to last week's top priority. Some of us think priorities are based on the latest book he has read."

To avoid this leadership confusion, it's important that there be a clear focus. By taking the six steps below, you will be able to provide direction and clearly articulate your organizational priorities in the context of the mission and environment.

Six critical steps for making service excellence a priority

Creating and maintaining a culture of service excellence won't happen by chance; it can only be achieved by design. Approaching your plan with specific goals in mind will help predict your success. While some of these steps may appear to be little more than common sense, remember that the art and the science of real leadership often boil down to some very basic principles. The real test is to make sure they are applied and practiced consistently.

The following six steps are not rocket science, but they are among the common denominators of some of the most service-oriented health care organizations in the country. When executed consciously and consistently, they can help you propel your organization toward excellence.

1. Tie service excellence to mission, vision and values.
2. Clarify goals.
3. Hold others accountable for results.
4. Recognize and celebrate progress.
5. Develop cascading communication processes.
6. Lead by example.

1. Tie service excellence to mission, vision and values.

"Whether as an army, a nation, or a corporation - people become unstoppable when they are moved by a common vision and have the power and tools to achieve it."

- United Technologies Corporation

Whose priority is it, anyway? Leaders will have far fewer problems persuading staff to accept new challenges if it's clear how they fit into their own responsibilities and ultimately strengthen their individual sense of purpose. This individual connection, along with the connection to the organization's mission, vision and values, creates the unstoppable momentum described above.

Communicating priorities in context of mission, vision and values is an essential duty for leaders. If you don't communicate what is most important, you can't complain when goals aren't met. It is vital for a leader to be able to articulate the priorities of the organization and make a compelling case for daily operations that support the mission. It takes a conscious effort to continually bring customer service and other priorities to the forefront by connecting service back to the mission, vision and values.

Saying it once is not enough. Establish the priorities but don't forget to keep making the connection between daily activities, priorities and the goals.

Set your compass to true north

No matter where you release a homing pigeon, it will find its way home. And the mission swallows return every year - on the same day - to San Juan Capistrano. No one knows how, but some sort of inner homing device - like an internal GPS - guides them along their path.

Like these amazing creatures, each of us needs an internal compass to guide us and to give us direction. For most of us, this is a connection to purpose derived from our own values, which, when manifested into actions and integrated into daily life, is a prescription for happiness.

Recently, I completed my open water scuba-diving certification. As part of the curriculum, I had to learn to use a compass to navigate under water and to guide me back to my starting point. For anyone raised in the computer age with navigational devices and digital dashboard compasses, using an old-fashioned compass to set the course and return safely was a challenge. Even a few misguided kicks took me rapidly off course. And, once off course, it was difficult to course-correct.

When the water was clear, I had great visibility for yards. Using visual cues, I could see my landmarks and could course-correct. But when the water was murky, it was difficult to find my way. Eventually, and with coaching from my dive master, I was able to trust the compass and find my way, under even the murkiest conditions.

Like the diver who has learned to rely on the age-old navigational tool, leaders who set their course according to their mission, vision and values will be able to navigate more smoothly during rough times and pull their teams back on course.

More than any other service-related business, health care organizations need to foster a culture that guides their employees to live the mission in every action. But don't assume that if the mission statement is posted on every wall employees will innately understand how their individual roles relate to the mission, vision and values. As remedial as it may seem, senior leaders, managers, and supervisors need to clearly articulate how specific decisions and actions tie back to the mission, vision and values. The mission, vision and values must be the organization's true north.

My colleagues and I have worked in countless health care organizations that were not using their mission, vision and values as a compass. In these cases, the mission was posted on the wall like any other certificate or artwork. After a while, no one even saw the words - they were unrelated to anything of importance and blended into the woodwork. In other cases, the leaders talked loosely about the mission but failed to anchor it to daily priorities and resource allocation.

An organization that uses the mission in this manner is like a scuba diver who leaves his compass tucked inside his vest pocket and then wonders how he got so badly off course. Keep it visible - not just on the wall, but as the foundation for daily operations. Check back with it during key decisions. Filter your thoughts and actions through it, and you will be strengthening your own internal homing device.

Make your priority part of your first impression

But how do you make the information tangible and pertinent? One CEO I worked with spent the first hour of employee orientation discussing the mission, vision and values. The hospital's vision was "to be a place where patients choose to come for care, where physicians want to practice, and where employees want to work." This CEO offered a memorable message to the new recruits. He told them that if they always filtered their actions and decisions through that vision statement, they would always be on the right track. Now that's clarity. It's simple and memorable and a great reference point.

The Priority Pyramid

The model shown below is one that has been effective in helping health care leaders demonstrate how service excellence fits into the organizational structure. We chose a pyramid because it represents a structure that is strong and enduring over time. Like the ancient pyramids, organizations that stay connected to their mission, vision and values will not only be strong and enduring, but focused.

© Baird Consulting

This is the framework that we use when working with senior leaders of our health care organizations. It provides them a great visual to help everyone remember that their daily work is part of a bigger picture. Budgets are developed to achieve goals and objectives under each of the four cornerstones. By using this pyramid, leaders have an excellent tool to show how resources are allocated in the context of their organizations' mission, vision and values.

I worked in a community hospital that had a mission statement that was very clear in defining its purpose and commitment to the community. However, this organization had strayed far from the community, and its focus had been turned inward. After years of losing market share and suffering from community criticism, this hospital - and its new leadership - wanted desperately to turn things around.

To gain community support and trust, it was vital that the hospital return to its mission as its driving force. This return was not without resistance, however. When we announced that the hospital would be involved in more community benefit initiatives, one nurse at an employee forum said, "We are here to serve our patients. Why should we spend our time and money on this fluff? Sure, it's a nice thing to do, but it has nothing to do with our real purpose."

Her short statement spoke volumes about where the organization had been and where it needed to go. It had lost its inner compass and had drifted off course from its reason for existence. The employees saw their work as only the person in the bed in front of them, rather than as an integral part of an organization that had been created as a community resource.

Raising the bar:
Beryl puts customers first

Placing service excellence as a top priority is nothing new for Beryl. Being voted one of the country's best places to work is just one affirmation of the organization's unwavering commitment to excellence. CEO Paul Spiegelman's No. 1 priority is a culture strategy that places employees first.

Beryl provides call center services for health care organizations across the United States. Spiegelman knows that that a positive, productive work force doesn't just impact the Beryl culture, it has a direct impact on the reputations of every hospital that they serve.

"Because we are the call center for hospitals and medical practices, our staff is often the front door for patients in each hospital's community," says Spiegelman.

In an industry known for high turnover and low satisfaction, Beryl has managed to cut turnover and raise employee and customer satisfaction by setting very clear priorities and making sure that everyone lives up to them.

According to Spiegelman, "The most important thing that a leader can do is to state the course, then stay the course. No matter how much growth we have seen over the years, the thing that has kept us on task is our ability to stay the course. Every decision is tied to our mission statement and core values. It is our tradition and culture strategy that has gotten us where we are today. That tradition has been, and will continue to be, the core of who we are."

Spiegelman's company started in his parent's garage more than 20 years ago. Partnering with his two brothers, Spiegelman formed the call center company with one small account. Since that time, he has built an enterprise that currently manages hundreds of health care call centers translating into thousands of calls daily for hospitals and medical practices from coast to coast.

"We have a duty to live not only our own mission, but our clients' missions as well," says Spiegelman.

He further adds, "Consistency is a top priority because it ensures a quality encounter for every caller. There are obstacles to maintaining consistency and we need to constantly work through them. Consistency can be threatened by naysayers on staff, or a bad manager that impacts culture and turnover. Changes in the external business environment that require us to change course can also threaten consistency.

"We actually turned over the majority of our management team at one point as we entered into a growth mode. The business changed and so did our talent requirements. The challenge is, how do you take the organization's traditions and continue to lead in the spirit of those traditions, while navigating through change? I've learned that I can't ignore our traditions. They are a top priority. And no matter what changes we are navigating through, we must always turn our focus back to mission, culture and tradition. With those as our guideposts, we can more easily stay the course. We have found that when struggling with a big business decision, the answer becomes much clearer when we filter it through our mission," explains Spiegelman.

It's not enough to have people memorize the mission just to recite it back, says Spiegelman. "It's more important that everyone understands it, embraces it and lives it. Then, and only then, will it permeate the very core of our culture. It's just not enough to have the executive team promoting a mission-centered culture. Our supervisors and managers are vital to the culture. We have learned over time that in order to foster a healthy mission-centered culture, we have to hold managers accountable for improving employee satisfaction scores.

"Weaving the mission and vision into the culture comes down to trust," says Spiegelman. "People have to trust you and see that you mean what you say, and that you, too, are committed to living the mission. I continually reinforce the mission formally and informally during town hall meetings, in conversations while walking around the departments, and in my newsletter column. I very consciously repeat key words from the mission statement in conversations and articles so that people will make the connection between our mission, our priorities, and their jobs."

Living the promise

When my colleagues and I do "mystery shopping" for health care organizations, we try to gauge the customer experience not only according to generally accepted satisfaction criteria but also in the context of that organization's mission and vision statements, as well as its brand promise. This is incredibly important, because these statements tend to set the public's expectations of health care organizations - especially those that widely publicize these statements.

We're consistently amazed at the number of organizations that consider themselves to be mission-driven, yet demonstrate a sizable gap between customer experience and the printed promises. The gap often exists because a small, elite group crafts the lofty statement and doesn't formulate a plan for how they will infuse the words into the hearts and minds of their constituents. Or they send out a memo or have one meeting that describes the new branding campaign, mission statement or revised strategic plan and then expect everyone to automatically understand how it fits with daily operations.

A tool to apply now

When your advertising tagline uses words like "compassion," "care" and "service," you are setting expectations. Try this: Ask yourself what each of those words looks like to you as a consumer. If you have been promised compassion, care and service, imagine walking through the doors of an urgent care unit and describe what you experience. Write down your expectations:
• What would you expect as you walk through the doors?
• What do you expect to see?
• Who do you expect to see?
• How do the people around you behave?
• How do they interact with you?
• What do you expect them to do to manage your discomfort?
• How are they communicating with you?

Now take your list of expectations and do a reality check. Walk through the doors of the urgent care unit and test your operations on the basis of these expectations that were established by your own advertising tagline. Or, for a more objective view, send in mystery shoppers as patients and have them evaluate their experiences.

Once you have the real experiences, identify the gap between expectations and experience. This exercise is an extremely valuable one to work through with department staff. Managers in every department can take the mission and vision statements, as well as the advertising tagline, and do this exercise with staff in order to help them to define and understand how their work is directly connected.

We have had so many valuable experiences helping health care providers to see the gap between their promises and the actual patient experience that if I tried to put them all down on paper, I would have volumes of stories. But for the purpose of brevity, one such story stands out in my memory.

If everything speaks, what are you saying?

My colleagues and I had been conducting an assessment of a multi-specialty medical practice for a few days. While some members of my team were doing mystery shopping, I was conducting interviews with the physicians and managers to learn more about the culture.

I noticed that in virtually every department I visited, there was a framed document entitled, "Our Promise." The document had an eloquent description of what patients could expect from their experience with both their individual providers and the organization as a whole. The promise contained words like "privacy," "dignity," "respect" and "prompt access." Reading the promise, I was convinced that this medical practice held service excellence as a top priority. According to the document, staff members were living a shining example of patient-centered care.

Imagine my surprise when I learned that the mystery shoppers, who had made phone calls to schedule appointments and had been seen as patients, reported grossly contrasting experiences that did not even remotely resemble what was described in the promise.

For starters, the wait time for appointments was upwards of 13 weeks in some of the most competitive specialties. What happened to the promise of "prompt access?"

In the elevator, we spotted a yield sign instructing passengers to give the right-of-way to patients on gurneys. I was a bit baffled because I don't usually see a high volume of patients being wheeled through clinics on gurneys. When I asked about the sign and why I was seeing an occasional gurney being wheeled from the public elevator back to the exam room area, I was told, "Some of our doctors don't want to go next door to see patients at the hospital. If they get too busy, they just ask to have the patients brought over here."

Because the building was set up as a clinic and not as an inpatient facility, none of the transportation routes were private. So patients wearing hospital gowns were being paraded through public waiting areas. What happened to the promises of "privacy," "dignity" and "respect?"

The fact that this practice was deemed acceptable spoke volumes about the culture. The real irony was that no one there had ever considered that anything was wrong with the practice of dragging inpatients out of their rooms and over to the clinic for an exam that could, and should, take place in the privacy of their hospital rooms. Shifting their mindset from physician-centered to patient-centered was nothing short of a Herculean challenge.

The hospital that shared the same campus as the clinic, and was physically connected to this clinic, had many of the same practices. It was not unusual to see patients being wheeled from a transport vehicle through the front doors. It was easier for the transport staff, but it did nothing to protect the privacy of the patient that was being paraded across a patio and through the front lobby.

If your vision is really something to which you aspire, make sure you are living it. It's not enough to have a mission statement, value statement or promise posted. Posting it doesn't make it a reality. In fact, posting it makes you all the more accountable for making the words a reality. You have to be ready to live up to your promise with every process, every policy and every encounter. We have developed a memorable symbol and catch phrase related to living the mission, promise and tagline. We call it "E to the third power" and it is a visual reminder to strive for consistency in everything we do.

© Baird Consulting

Raising the bar:
Medical City defies gravity

As CEO of Medical City and Medical City Children's Hospital in Dallas, Texas, Britt Berrett has led an impressive turnaround in only a few short years. Berrett has made several important discoveries along his journey toward service excellence. Among those discoveries is that courage is one of the most fundamental leadership qualities required for success. He found that it takes courage to dream big, set a new direction and never waver from the target.

"When it comes to leading a culture of excellence, a CEO has tremendous responsibility. A passion for excellence cannot be delegated to someone else. It's an inspired stewardship," says Berrett. "I am passionate about health care, because every day in the course of our work, we are blessing the lives of patients. A CEO who expects and demands excellence must have it in his heart and be uncompromising and zealous in his quest for excellence, almost to the point of sacrificing his career for the good of the whole."

When Berrett stepped into his role, he set clear priorities and courageously kept Medical City accountable for results. Berrett is innately passionate about service, but in order to propel the organization toward excellence, he had to be able to articulate the goals and generate enthusiasm for success. It was natural for him to dream big enough and form a compelling vision that engaged others into becoming part of the vision.

"People want to work with winners," Berrett says. "If you can articulate a compelling vision, people will want to be involved in making the vision a reality. That is the art of transformational leadership. If you are enthusiastic and charismatic with a compelling vision, people will want to join you in your cause."

Berrett realized that not everyone dreams big or envisions greatness. "I had to help people learn to dream big," he says. "At one point, I asked our leadership team to list all of the awards and recognitions that they could ever want or hope to achieve. Some of them didn't have any idea what was possible. In this case, it was a matter of helping our team to realize that there was a whole world of possibilities out there just waiting for them. Once they started to learn about awards and recognition, they started to see the value of stretching their vision beyond what they knew and into the future. In the process, they stopped settling for being good and started pushing for great."

In his early days with Medical City, Berrett and his senior team developed the "five keys to the city:"

- Employee pride
- Patient loyalty
- Physician engagement
- Fiscal performance
- Commitment to the community

"Quality is a part of all of the five keys," explains Berrett. "We incorporate quality measures in each key area, which allows us to compare ourselves against benchmarks and set goals accordingly." Berrett made it his personal mission to make sure that every employee of Medical City and Medical City Children's Hospital understood the keys as the top priorities of the organization. Under each of the keys were specific goals and action plans designed to move the organization from good to great.

The organization's success has been significant. Patient satisfaction moved from the bottom quartile to the top 10 percent, explains Berrett.

"Measures of physician engagement are still steadily improving, and financial performance has shifted from a mediocre and unimpressive performance in 2000, to spectacular results over the past several years. In addition to that, we have seen great employee engagement both internally and in their commitment to community service," he says.

Courageous focus on mission and priorities sometimes put Berrett in the hot seat. "We expect that employees participate in

some form of community service. That is built right into their performance appraisals," says Berrett. "At first, people looked at me like
I was nuts, but when they started to see how it ties to the mission
and organizational vision, it made sense. Now it is a way of life."

By investing in better staffing the nursing departments, Berrett
knew that Medical City would exceed its budget by a significant
amount. Still, Berrett forged ahead in spite of the gap. "It was the
right thing to do, so I stood behind my team's decision and supported them," Berrett says. "That's not easy to do when you are accountable for the bottom line. But we were focused on the vision and our
priorities, so it was clearly the right decision."

Berrett is clear that passion is the catalyst that drives leaders to
achieve a vision. He feels that it must be encouraged in others as
well. But Berrett has also made an interesting observation about the
need to cultivate and direct passion in order to avoid dissonance. We
need leaders who are passionate about their work and their purpose,
but not so passionate that they become destructive, Berret explains.
"If passion is not embraced, cultivated and directed, it can be
destructive. Leaders have to help direct the passion in order to avoid
silos."

Berrett shares a story of how he once intervened between a
nursing unit and materials management. The materials management
team members were passionate about their responsibility to deliver
the right supplies to the right place in the right timeframe. They
were adamant about the need for tracking and good inventory control. At the same time, the nurses on the unit were not being attentive to scanning supplies, because they were more focused on the
patient care than the inventory control.

Both teams were passionate about their purpose. Neither was
right or wrong, but in order to successfully resolve the issue, they
had to view the challenge from a new perspective. Berrett coached
the two teams to screen the problem through this question: "What
can we do differently to bless the lives of the patients we serve?"

Framing the problem from that perspective helped both parties to engage in constructive problem solving. The two teams were able to solve their imminent problem and go on to collaborate on other pressing issues. From what started as a heated discussion and blame game, came a great solution to an age-old problem: tracking down missing wheelchairs, blood pressure cuffs, IV poles and pulse oximeters. The teams solved that problem by placing radio frequency chips on all the movable items, so that now, a nurse can lay her hands on any item she needs within seconds.

Berrett is a leader who exudes passion for his work while maintaining a clear focus on the organization's top priorities. In short, he says, "Achieving the vision takes innovation, passion, and pursuit of excellence. If you can practice transformational leadership that engages everyone in the vision, you can defy gravity."

2. Clarify goals: If you can measure it, you can move it!

"The reason most people never reach their goals is that they don't define them, or ever seriously consider them as believable or achievable. Winners can tell you where they are going, what they plan to do along the way, and who will be sharing the adventure with them."

- Denis Watley

When your staff has very clear target goals, they are able to stay focused on what is most important.

My colleagues and I have worked in several organizations that do a poor job of setting and communicating clear goals for service. Organizational leaders bring us in to help them with their patient satisfaction. One of the first questions we ask is, "What are your goals?" More than once, that question has been answered with a vague response such as, "To raise our scores! They are in the basement right now."

As remedial as it may sound, leaders need to be able to articulate the specifics of the goal. First, is it the scores that you want to raise? Or is your real goal to improve the actual patient experience that is reflected in the scores? There is a difference.

Jeanne Bliss, author of "Chief Customer Officer: Getting Past Lip Service to Passionate Action" (2006 Jossey Bass), wrote an article, "Are You a Customer Service Score Whore?" (Marketing Profs, www.marketing profs.com/6/bliss4.asp). Bliss' shocking title grabs the reader's attention while exposing one of the biggest pitfalls of satisfaction measurement. She cites examples of companies that tie scores to compensation and, in the process, shift staff focus to the score, rather than to the experience behind the score.

Bliss asks the crucial question: "Is your commitment to customers real - or a jockeying for position on the latest customer scoreboard?" She goes on to write: "The target keeps changing names, but the game's the same. The name of the game should be 'giving customers a memory and experience so great that they'll want to repeat it.' But sadly, the game is all about getting that score - that darned customer score - any way possible."

The intention may be good; tie compensation to the satisfaction scores and everyone will rally around to make sure that the customer has a great experience and will give us the best score - right? Not always. When the goal is all about the score, and the score is tied to compensation, people will go out of their way to game the system any way they can.

One hospital put such emphasis on the scores that people forgot why they were measuring in the first place. Trying to get everyone to move their average scores from fours to fives, they created buttons for employees to wear that said, "Strive for Five." The intention was to make the experience one that would be worthy of the highest patient score. But the way it played out was quite different.

One patient reported that when she asked a nursing assistant what the button meant, the assistant told her, "It has to do with our raises. If you get a survey and score us all fives, we'll get a raise. If you don't, we won't get the raise." From this nursing assistant's point of view, the issue was all about the raise. From the patient perspective, she felt pressured to score them all fives or she'd be depriving this poor nursing assistant of a raise.

This is not unlike the auto dealer who calls after an encounter to find out how satisfied you were with the experience. What often starts as a customer-focused courtesy call sometimes ends up with prodding, if not pleading, to give the best possible marks, should you be called by the corporate office.

Get clear about your goals and how you are communicating them

I was speaking to a group of managers one day and was dumbstruck by one's comment. She said, "We are getting so many mixed messages about different priorities. I don't know if I am supposed to focus on our Press Ganey scores or customer service." Ouch! How did their goals get so disconnected? Somewhere along the line the leaders lost sight of why they were measuring patient satisfaction in the first place.

Watch your words

If you continually talk about raising your survey scores rather than improving patient satisfaction, your language is emphasizing the score over the goal. I can't imagine any of my nursing school instructors telling me that the goal was to score well on my boards instead of reinforcing solid comprehension and critical thinking skills to ensure that I was delivering the best possible care for my patients. The scores were a reflection of what I knew and how I could perform.

As leaders, we need to make sure that we are putting the spotlight on the right things. Set the goals clearly, but make sure that people know how the goals are tied to what is most important - the patient experience and personal satisfaction. It is important for staff to understand that they will be happier delivering the kind of service that resonates most with the customer.

Make goals measurable and specific

Stating the goal in specific, measurable terms will help everyone clarify where they are going, how far they have to travel, and in what time frame.

A goal stated like this gives the specific target information needed: "To raise our overall mean for patient satisfaction from 83 to 86 by January." You may even want to be more specific about one area of the survey, such as likelihood of recommending: "Our goal is to raise the score on the question, 'Likelihood of recommending' from 81 percent to 97 percent over the next 18 months." But always emphasize that the score is only a reflection of the patient experience. The overarching goal is to improve the patient experience as evidenced by an improvement in the score.

Break goals into bite-size pieces

Once the overall goal is set, help departments or service lines drill down into the factors that influence why a patient would want to recommend them. Get staff involved in understanding the experiences that leave their patients feeling good about their experience. In the Chapter Three (Processes), I will be delving deeper into how to get staff more involved in achieving goals through the SWAT process.

If you throw out a goal without connecting it back to each department's performance and each individual's role, people won't understand the connection between a score and customer service. Nothing will change, and you will spend years chasing that elusive score.

Tie service goals to the big picture

Your team will be able to see the connection between the scores and the organizational vision if you tell them, "We want to be a place where patients choose to come for care, where physicians want to practice and where employees want to work. That means setting goals in each of those areas."

One of the successful techniques we use with senior leaders is to conduct a "visioning" session in which they are encouraged to envision the future as they wish it to be. From there, we back into drafting specific goals to make that vision a reality. As basic as this may sound, it is a step that is frequently glossed over or done without much thought. When the leaders have a clear vision, they are much more likely to feel impassioned about it and will be able to motivate others much more easily into striving for that goal as well.

Using the Priority Pyramid shown on page 7, the senior leaders create specific goals under each cornerstone. These goals will become the basis for ongoing accountability. Although this concept is not new or unique, it is far too often skipped or disconnected from the big picture. There are four conerstones for organizational success:

Clinical quality - What specific clinical goals are you striving to improve? What metrics will be used? How will you communicate this goal? How will you tie this goal to departmental performance?

Work force strength - What are you doing to improve the work environment and how will the progress be measured? This can be depicted in turnover, retention or employee satisfaction survey scores. How are you communicating efforts to improve?

Financial performance - How is the organization measuring financial performance? Rather than focusing on complex ratios, consider articulating this as cost per adjusted patient day (hospitals) or cost per patient visit. Communicate how day-to-day operations can have a direct impact on this goal.

Service excellence - What is your method for measuring customer satisfaction? State the target goal. Rather than focus solely on patient satisfaction, identify benchmarks for each constituent group, including physicians, patients, referral sources and payers.

Capture the heart

One common mistake many leaders make when setting goals is that they craft lofty goals that appeal to the intellect rather than the heart. They'll proudly display charts, graphs, statistics and metrics of all kinds. From there, the cerebral leader will try to lecture, urge, cheerlead or even threaten people to meet the goals. But where is the appeal to the heart?

Think about the kinds of people who choose to work in health care. While they often are intelligent, results-driven individuals, they are also motivated by the sense that they are making a difference, a contribution to the greater good. The concept of engaging the heart and helping others to develop a connection to purpose will be covered in more depth in Chapter Four (Purpose). But there is value in engaging the imagination as well.

Capturing a spirit of innovation is a strategy that is likely to strengthen engagement, build ownership and produce results. More about fostering innovation is covered in the Process chapter.

Tom Morris, author of "The Art of Achievement" (2002, MJF Books), captures the concept eloquently. He writes, "Lead with your heart and by your head. Lead your own life down the paths you choose with the lure of imaginative vision, and you can lead others the same way."

This is the art and the science of leadership. When you use your imagination to envision a brighter future and you articulate that vision clearly and with enthusiasm, others will want to be a part of that journey.

Are they the right goals?

Once you have set your goals, it's important to stay the course if - and only if - the goals are the right ones. But, let's face it – sometimes we catch ourselves heading down the wrong path. Don't be afraid to course-correct. Just because you set a certain goal doesn't mean that that goal will always remain the most pertinent or the highest priority. The environment is constantly changing, and you must be strong enough, clear enough, and yet humble enough to change course if and when you need to. We all make decisions based on the information at hand. When things change, you need to be able to change as well. There is no shame in admitting that you have changed as a result of having new information.

In medicine, protocols change constantly as we integrate new data. Although few people embrace change wholeheartedly, most recognize the need to make adjustments based on the latest research.

Our firm worked with one hospital system with the following service excellence goal: "The composite satisfaction with nursing score will be above the 75th percentile in all nursing units throughout the system." Because the nurses' scores were singled out, they felt they were in the hot seat. Several nurses told me that they felt this was unfair and unrealistic. To them, it made a statement that everyone else was off the hook for service. At the same time, an organization-wide success share was offered for achieving that goal, which only placed more pressure on the nursing staff.

To the leaders who set this goal, it made perfect sense. They rationalized that if patients were pleased with their nursing care, they would be pleased with their overall experience. While there may have been some logic to this, there was also a cost: Every quarter, when the patient satisfaction reports arrived, everyone was focusing on the five questions pertaining to nursing and on almost nothing else. The nurses felt singled out, but put forth their best efforts to make positive strides. The impact was impressive, and nearly every nursing unit achieved the goal, but not without some resentment. They believed they were under greater pressure to achieve the customer service goals than anyone else in the system.

After nearly two years with the nursing goal as their No. 1 service goal, the system shifted the focus to likelihood of recommending and overall satisfaction in order to engage everyone in their service efforts. Was the nursing goal wrong? Chances are that the nursing questions would be closely correlated to overall satisfaction and likelihood of recommending anyway. But in light of their culture and the feedback from the nursing staff, the leader had the chance to course-correct and state the goals in terms that would encompass all departments and service.

3. Hold others accountable for results.

I think of accountability as being a close first cousin of priority. A great leader cannot say something is a priority and then not hold himself and others accountable for operating in accordance with that stated priority. Simply stating goals just isn't enough. You need to let people know how they will be held accountable and over what period of time.

For example, if your goal is to raise your overall mean score from 83 to 86 by January of 2009, tell your supervisors and managers how often you will be taking a "pulse check" with them on the measurements and what feedback they can expect from you.

If quarterly updates are your method for keeping tabs on progress, let the managers and supervisors know what process you will be implementing to ensure that everyone is focused on the right goals. Let them know:

- **Who** will be reviewing managers' and departments' progress?
- **What** metrics will be used? What are the consequences for not making progress? What support is available?
- **When** is the target date for achieving the goal? Are there incremental goals along the way?
- **Why** is this important to the organization?
- **How** will each person measure his or her results? How will each leader achieve his or her specific goals? How will each leader engage staff in making specific measurable improvements in their department?

I once told a CEO, "It's not what a leader expects, it's what he inspects." He grimaced at this and said, "I hate the concept of babysitting. I shouldn't have to do that. These are professional adults." He was right about the age bracket and the professional qualifications, but that was the extent of it since the results across all the organization's strategic goals showed it wasn't getting the results it needed. And most of the shortfalls could be traced directly to management performance. So I said, "Okay, so how is your autonomous approach working for you?"

You need to make a commitment to putting a process for accountability in place and then stay with the cycle of inspection.

Accountability can be a tough challenge, especially for organizations that have not had a high degree of accountability in the past. All of a sudden, there's a new sheriff in town - and he means business. It may not actually be new leadership at all, but a new leadership perspective, that jolts the organization into a new level of accountability.

We worked with one organization and listened to the senior leadership team complain bitterly about incompetence of their management team. During the assessment phase of our engagement we heard about the managers' marginal performance from senior leaders, fellow managers and physicians. I remember thinking, "Hmmm. This is not rocket science, folks." But I let them talk so I could gather the necessary information.

I'll never forget the expressions on the faces of the senior leaders when I stood before them and said, "I've heard from you, as well as other sources, that many of your managers are not suited for their roles." Heads nodded around the table. So I continued, "And I've heard that this group of poor performers accounts for about one third of all of your managers. Is that true?" Again a round of nods. So I came in with the big question. "Well, who do they work for?"

Ouch. There was no escaping the harsh reality that the problem was sitting around the table. They were getting exactly what they had been rewarding. Somebody was giving these poor performing managers their annual evaluations. Somebody was approving their salaries, benefits and budget. And those "somebodies" were sitting right there at the table complaining about poor performance.

The bottom line is this: You have to be ready to make the tough decisions in spite of the discomfort involved. You might have worked with these people for years. You might really like them. But every day that you tolerate their marginal performance you are eroding your own credibility.

Accountability starts with being very clear about what you want, from whom, and by when. Then, follow up. Don't lay out expectations if you have no intention of following up with rewards and consequences. That will only erode your credibility.

I was at a meeting recently where senior leaders from across the country were comparing ways in which they held their managers accountable for results. One person explained that all leaders within her health system were expected to submit 90-day plans outlining their action steps for helping the organization achieve its strategic goals. But in addition to the written plan, twice a month during the management update meetings, each manager was to stand up and tell the rest of the management team what actions they had completed in the last two weeks to fulfill their plan.

No one was allowed to talk about what he or she planned to do or what was being considered or explored. They had to focus strictly on what they had actually done. If they did not have something specific to report, they had to stand up and say, "Pass." Using this round-robin approach, managers were publicly accountable to their peers for their actions. No one wanted to have to pass and publicly admit that he or she was not living up to his or her own plan.

Accountability doesn't end with your expectations of your management team. A culture of accountability permeates every level of the organization. That means having very clear expectations for performance and then holding staff accountable for living up to those expectations. It's one thing to tell your managers that they are accountable for raising patient satisfaction scores in their units, but it's an entirely different feeling when a leader paves the way for accountability for each and every individual on the team. That means that all the individuals in the organization know what's expected of them and understand how those expectations are tied to organizational and departmental goals and their own performance criteria.

Standards - a baseline for accountability

Creating service standards is an absolutely essential component in a culture of service excellence. But in order to be actionable and sustainable, the standards must be written as behavioral, measurable and observable. In addition, the standards can't be viewed as a separate document that people look at once, nod in agreement and then put out of their minds. Rather, the standards must be infused into daily practices. That means including standards in job descriptions, performance appraisals and key messages.

I have seen many organizations struggle with accountability. When I ask them about standards, I am told, "Oh, we have had customer service standards for years." But on closer inspection, I observe that what they have is a list of words that have no link to real accountability. More often than not, the words fit nicely into an acronym that everyone can remember, but that is the end of it. I've seen lists of standards that fit neatly into acronyms such as RESPECT, CARE, SERVE, and numerous other service-minded words.

But a list of words is just that - a list. If you want to foster a culture of accountability, specific behaviors must be associated with every one of those words and those behaviors must be tied to specific, observable performance indicators on which every employee will be judged. Without that, the standards are just one more lofty-worded document that people see once and forget.

We have worked with countless organizations that come to us for help after struggling for years. They have some of the pieces in place but cannot seem to get the traction they need in order to move to the next level. The first thing we look at is their set of standards to see how they are infused into the organization. More often than not, the struggling organizations have a list that stands separate from any form of accountability, such as the job descriptions and performance appraisals.

One small hospital we worked with was very proud that it had had standards since the early 1990s. These standards fit neatly into the word RESPECT, and they were posted throughout the organization. But when I observed staff interaction with each other and their patients, it was clear that the standards were not top-of-the mind. The list of words was not behavior-based, observable, or measurable; nor were the words connected to job descriptions, performance appraisals, recognition or training. The list had nothing to do with their encounters.

When I asked senior leaders how the standards had been incorporated into job descriptions and performance appraisals, they told me that they had planned to get around to it but it was a lot of work to make that change. This is a prime example of how one seemingly simple step creates an unnecessary obstacle.

Many of the leadership principles essential in raising the bar on service excellence are not rocket science. In fact, most of them are fairly simple, just not easy. That theme seems to permeate virtually every aspect of life. Think about the person that loses 150 pounds. When asked how he did it he says, "It was fairly simple. I cut my calories and exercised regularly." Simple concept? Absolutely. Easy to execute on a daily basis and stay the course? Hardly.

Knowing something is important and doing it religiously are two different things. The issue of standards is one such issue. How can you expect to create consistently positive customer experiences if the standards are not clear, measurable, observable and infused into the culture? Make your standards your priorities.

But attaching standards to job descriptions and performance appraisals doesn't mean that they are infused into the hearts and minds of every employee and physician. It just means that you have taken one crucial step toward making your priority known and consistent throughout the organization.

Make the standards part of the language

Leaders must be creative in bringing the standards to life on a daily basis. Practice regularly incorporating the standards in your feedback discussion and recognition. For example, rather than saying, "Kathie, good job helping that family today," the manager can say, "Kathie, good job living our communication standard today. The way you prepared the Garcia family for Maria's discharge is a great example of communicating effectively. You made sure that they understood everything that was about to happen." In this example, the manager is offering recognition and reinforcement for specific actions tied to a specific standard. In doing so, the employee is making a conscious connection. The connections may be obvious to you, but they are not always obvious to others. By pointing out this link, you are helping to keep the priority front and center.

The other often-missed opportunity for tying standards to daily activity is sharing patient letters and survey comments with staff. Many managers post letters and surveys, but to infuse standards into the culture's language, try this exercise. In addition to reading or posting a survey comment or letter, ask staff to determine which standards have been met, exceeded or breeched in this patient experience.

This method can be used with both positive and negative feedback from patients. By having the discussion in the context of your standards, you are helping the staff to recognize the standards as they relate to the actual patient experience. Regular discussions about how the standards relate to the patient experience build greater awareness of the standards and demonstrates you are holding staff accountable for living the standards.

Example:

A. Imagine that you have received the following letter. Read it aloud to your staff during a staff meeting.

Dear Kris,
I want to personally thank the nurses on 2 South for their compassionate
care of my father, Robert Filmer, while he was on your unit. Two nurses in
particular stood out. They are Sharon on the day shift and Colleen on the
night shift. Both women took time to help us understand how to care for
dad at home. In fact, Sharon called us once dad got home to find out how he
was doing. We were really impressed by that. It shows that you really care.

We did want to mention that the only downfall of the experience was that
the call light was not working. Several times we mentioned it, but it was
never fixed. That caused us to feel uncertain about leaving dad because we
were afraid that if he needed something, he would have no way to get help.
Even though we were pleased with the care, we wanted you to know that the
call light was a problem for us.

Please send our thanks to all of your great staff. They are the best!

Sincerely,

Mary Filmer

*B. After reading the letter to your staff, ask them to identify statements
or comments that relate to specific standards. Below, staff underlined
the statements indicated above.*

*C. Once the statements have been identified, ask them to state which
standard the statement relates to. In this case, staff identified:*

Communicate effectively - helped us understand how to care for dad at home (E)
Make a lasting last impression- Sharon called us once dad got home (E)
Be responsive to concerns- we mentioned it, but it was never fixed (B)
Offer Reassurance - caused us to feel uncertain about leaving; would have no way to
get help (B)

*D. After identifying which standards relate to the letter, ask if the stan-
dards had been met (M), exceeded (E) or breeched (B) in each example.*

E. In situations where the standard has been exceeded, the manager can use this opportunity to thank and recognize the individuals mentioned. In cases where the standard was breeched, ask the staff to discuss ideas for how they can improve the situation to prevent future dissatisfaction.

4. Recognize and celebrate progress

In every organization, there are people who rise to the occasion and shine. When you recognize and celebrate these stars, you are publicly reminding everyone that when they focus on priorities, they will be recognized. When you recognize others for their service efforts, it is one more way you are demonstrating that service is a priority for you and for the organization.

Recognition can be as simple as walking around the department and personally thanking people for completing a project, or it can be as personal as a handwritten note. When I do workshops, I typically ask the audience (which is usually made up of leaders) if they have ever personally received a thank-you note from their boss. Asking for a show of hands, I then ask them to keep their hand in the air if they had kept the note. Every time I ask that question, virtually 100 percent of those who indicated that they had received a thank-you note also confirmed that they'd saved the note. My unofficial research demonstrates that a personal thank-you note is highly valued.

Many articles and books have been written on the subject of rewarding and recognizing employees. The tactics are as many and varied as health care settings themselves. Rather than elaborate on what can be done to recognize employees, let me just reinforce that recognition is one more way that you can put your priorities into action and make them visible to all those around you.

I mentioned quarterly plans as a means of holding managers accountable for results, but they are also a great way to identify and recognize supervisors and managers who are making measurable progress. Identify them and spotlight success stories in management meetings.

By publicly recognizing managers who have made positive changes, you are publicly reinforcing that service is a priority and will be recognized.

If you have a company intranet site, use it to spotlight teams that are making positive changes. Post the team photo along with their goals and results. They can be shared as your internal best practices and will provide a great opportunity for peer-to-peer coaching between departments.

Recognition should be prompt, personal, pertinent and plentiful. In other words, don't wait for the annual review to give praise and recognition; do it promptly following the event and make it specific to the person, the event and the behavior. Tie your recognition back to the organizational goals whenever possible. And don't be stingy! Recognition needs to happen often, with sincerity and in context of goals and strategies.

A friend of mine talks about growing up in a staunch German community in Minnesota. The culture there didn't promote much in the way of demonstrative behavior. He jokes about how stingy people in that culture are with their compliments and how guarded they are against revealing any emotion. He tells of a man, married for 50 years, reflecting on his long, blissful marriage to the most wonderful woman in the world. He said, "I love my wife so much, I almost told her once."

Is that how you are with recognition? Are you holding back on recognition or using it to build the kind of culture that supports a vision of excellence? Ask yourself how you can raise the bar on recognition and keep tabs on how often you give recognition.

One way to keep track of how often you reinforce and recognize is to start each day with 10 pennies in a change purse in your pocket. Every time you offer recognition to someone, move a penny from the change purse to your pocket. At the end of the day, see if you are still holding tight to your pennies or if you have moved them. It's a great way to make change with change.

Different sources for recognition include leader-to-staff member, peer-to-peer, or patient-to-staff. Regardless of the source, link the recognition back to the organizational mission, vision, goals, or standards in order to help people make the connection between their behaviors, the big picture goals and the culture.

5. Cascading communication

When it comes to feeding a thriving service-centered culture, what should you communicate? The short answer is: everything! The longer answer is: everything in context of your overall goals, mission, vision, and values. There is an art and a science to communication within complex organizations. You want to keep information front and center, but you don't want to overload the audience. This makes it all the more important that your messages are tied back to mission, vision and values.

Losing touch with your employees can be one of the biggest barriers to sustaining a vital customer-centered culture. Furthermore, when employees aren't informed, they won't be engaged.

Repetition is key

Posting goals once isn't enough to motivate lasting change. Leadership requires that we keep the needs of our constituents in mind at all times. Among those core needs are the need for information, the need to feel connected and the need to understand what makes our work worthwhile. Communication is the leader's catalyst for meeting all of those needs. Use every opportunity to communicate with purpose. Use a variety of communication tools to continually reinforce messages about the organizational mission, vision, values, standards and priorities. Share stories that demonstrate how individuals and departments are making improvements and moving toward organizational goals. You can tell these stories in face-to-face encounters as well as in newsletters and intranet postings.

Continually challenge yourself to find better ways of connecting the most vital information through your communications. Consciously seek opportunities to demonstrate what impact day-today activities have on the overall goals. In doing so, you will be help-ing each individual to understand how they connect to success and, in turn, will be moving your organization from good to great.

One of the biggest mistakes we make in communications is thinking that just because we have sent a message once, everyone has received that message and it has resonated at the deepest level. We are all humans, and we are living in an age where we are bombarded with messaging constantly. From the moment we wake up in the morning, until we drift off to sleep at night, we are deluged with messages everywhere!

I noticed this after returning from a scuba-diving trip to the Virgin Islands. While there, I had no phone service and limited Internet. My only means of transportation was my two feet. After living simply for just one week, I realized just how overwhelming our world of instant communications can be. It started with my refrigerator on my first day back home. I put my glass under the water dispenser, only to see a message flash, telling me that the filter needed to be changed. My BlackBerry beeped, telling me my next conference call was to start in 30 minutes. The computer reported that I had 15 new e-mail messages, and as the phone rang, I looked at the caller ID to see that it was my mother calling. Driving to my first appointment, the GPS told me where to turn, and the bill-boards along the highway flashed messages ranging from hair salons, to plastic surgeons, to Planned Parenthood - even a Bible passage. Is it any wonder we sometimes feel a bit overwhelmed?

One CEO posted his monthly message outside his office and told me he had done a thorough job of communicating. I asked him how often he went to the dietary department to read the bulletin board or to a nursing unit to review all of the memos. Of course, this is something that he didn't do routinely, if at all. Yet he was relying on foot traffic and basic curiosity to relay some of his most vital information.

Another favorite example is the CEO who puts his message in the newsletter once a year and feels he's covered all the organizational priorities, strategic plan, mission, vision and values (It's in print, so my job is done.) If something is truly a priority, it must be communicated over and over in a variety of ways, and through a variety of media.

Perhaps the greatest communication challenge for leaders is knowing how to cut through all the clutter with clear, concise, yet inspiring messages that resonate in the hearts of our constituents. Communication is a necessary component in virtually all of the five principles needed to raise the bar on service excellence in your culture. Communication helps to:

- Clarify and position the organization's priorities
- Engage people
- Improve understanding of processes changes and how they relate to goals
- Foster a sense of purpose in individuals within the organization
- Demonstrate leadership passion for excellence

If you are not a good communicator, get help. A leader needs to be able to get key messages across, not only to impart information on a cognitive level, but to inspire the heart as well. Turn to your in-house PR and communications staff to help you improve your writing and speaking skills. If you are uncomfortable seeking help from in-house staff, consider engaging a coach who can help you learn to articulate clearly, concisely, and with confidence.

Hone your storytelling skills

I have known passionate leaders who froze at the thought of having to tell a story in front of a crowd. Yet storytelling has an immense impact on the listener.

In the December 2007 issue of Harvard Business Review article, "The Four Truths of the Storyteller" (Reprint R0712C), author Peter Guber discusses the value of storytelling in leadership. Guber emphasizes that the value of storytelling isn't exclusive to formal presentations. He writes, "Whether the audience is a handful of colleagues or clients at lunch, or 10,000 convention-goers listening to a formal address, the secrets of a great story are largely the same" (p.55).

The HBR article emphasizes that business leaders often under-value or under estimate the impact of a good story. Guber points out two common misconceptions among business people: "First, many think it is purely about entertainment. But the use of the story, not only to delight, but also to instruct and lead, has long been a part of human culture," Guber says. "We can trace it back thousands of years to the days of the shaman around the tribal fire. It was he who recorded the oral history of the tribe, encoding its beliefs, values and rules in the tales of its great heroes, of it triumphs and tragedies. The life-or-death lessons necessary to perpetuate the community's sur-vival were woven into these stories. As a modern shaman, the vision-ary business leader taps into the human yearning to be part of a wor-thy cause."

The second common misconception among business leaders is that storytelling is just about fiction. "People assume that story-telling is somehow in conflict with authenticity. The great story-teller in this view is a spinner of yarns that amuse without being rooted in truth," Guber writes. "But great storytelling does not con-flict with truth. In the business world and elsewhere, it is always built on the integrity of the story and its teller. Hence, the emphasis is on the truth as its touchstone."

Even if you aren't a good storyteller now, that doesn't mean you should call it quits. Get help. There are numerous books and story-telling coaches who can help you. Storyteller coach Doug Lipman has written several books and numerous articles designed to enhance storytelling skills. His company, Story Dynamics (www.sto-rydynamics.com), is devoted to helping people in all walks of life to learn to tell clear and commanding stories that move and transform listeners. Annette Simmons' books also offer great pointers for improving your storytelling skills: "Whoever Tells the Best Story Wins" (2007 AMACOM) and "The Story Factor - Inspiration,

Influence and Persuasion Through the Art of Storytelling" (2006, Basic Books).

But live storytelling isn't the only communication tactic that will help you to keep organizational priorities out in front of your team. As a marketer I have long valued the multimedia approach to communicating key messages. It goes back to understanding how people learn. Some are strictly visual learners; they need to see things in order to absorb concepts. Others are auditory learners who retain more when they hear the messages. Then there are the experiential learners who learn best by being physically involved in an experience.

In addition to the many and varied learning styles, health care leaders are faced with a broad range of educational levels, age ranges and cultural differences within the work force. All of these have an impact on how messages are received.

The strategic Communication Planning Grid is one tool I have used over the years. It provides a framework for key messaging by identifying key stakeholders, considering stakeholders' points of view, planning the core message and establishing tactics to get that message across. Samples of the grid and example of how to use the grid are available on my website, www.baird-consulting.com, in the "articles" section.

Stakeholder Group	Stakeholder Point of View	Key Message	Tactics	Target Date	Assigned to:
Who has a vested interest in this issue?	*What is their core concern?*	*What specific information will help to address the stakeholders' core concerns?*	*How will you deliver the key messages?*	*When will this be completed?*	*Who will complete the tactic?*

The grid helps the user to define specific tactics that will be used to communicate with a variety of stakeholder groups over a period of time. It is important that leaders not think of communication as an isolated task. Communication crosses over into virtually every aspect of your organization, but is closely connected to all the elements of a service-centered culture. One message may cross over among multiple stakeholder groups.

Newsletters can cover a lot of territory, but don't put all your eggs in that communication basket. Use bulletin boards to post satisfaction scores and graphically depict progress. Highlight teams, their goals, progress, and successes in newsletters. Hold employee forums to offer the latest "state of the union," and make sure that you frame the meeting with mission, vision, goals, and priorities. Tell stories and use the opportunity to recognize individuals and celebrate organizational successes.

Communicate in context of goals

Many organizations create department bulletin boards depicting goals and current progress toward those goals. It's great to have a global view of the organization's goals, but make sure that your bulletin boards offer a "local" (department) slant in order to keep your staff feeling connected. Without the department link, you may fall victim to "corporate-speak."

Keep it local

We worked with one health system that had some beautifully polished publications and pre-formatted bulletin boards spotlighting their corporate goals and progress. But during focus groups, their employees expressed that they did not feel connected, informed, or engaged. This was pretty surprising since their progress and goals were on display. When we began to drill down into this phenomenon, the employees were quick to tell us that that they classified this type of communication tactic as "corporate-speak." They said that this type of message was too far removed from those at the outlying campuses.

Take a lesson from the newspaper industry in how you communicate between the corporate office, the local campus, and also at the department level. Although the local newspaper has world news, it still covers local stories and often will link the national news with a local slant. You can use the same tactic when bringing information from the corporate level down to the departmental level. Use the boards to spotlight your department members who are actively serving on SWAT teams (see Chapter Four, Processes) and show how their efforts are moving patient satisfaction scores or quality initiatives. Post short stories that feature your department associates who have been recognized for stellar performance. Post the most recent kudos from patients or other customers.

Communicate often

While it's easy to pinpoint some optimal times to communicate about customer service (such as when patient satisfaction results are released, or when an employee reaches a significant milestone), it's the day-to-day communication that will keep your employees engaged with, and interested in, customer service.

"Out of sight, out of mind" can easily apply to busy workers in today's health care organizations. While the majority entered their profession to help others, their daily task lists don't necessarily contain a specific entry designed to advance your customer service initiatives.

That's why it's important to make communicating customer service an integral part of daily life. Because the leaders responsible for communicating the customer service message are usually busy communicating many other organizational messages at the same time, it's essential they have the resources necessary to make customer service a top priority.

Cascading communication works best in face-to-face encounters. Our culture assessment focus groups reveal that in spite of the ready access to e-mail and online communications for instant bulletins, most employees still prefer to hear important information directly from their supervisors or managers. Whenever possible, give your department heads key talking points to relay to their staff.

Make sure they, in turn, are coaching supervisors on the same talking points. By giving department leaders the tools, they will have what they need to impart the most important information.

Is communication a core competency in your organization? If so, do all the managers and supervisors know that? Are they being held accountable for making sure that key messages are relayed in a timely, personal and pertinent manner? Do they have the tools that they need to help them disseminate vital information? As a leader, you cannot leave cascading communication to chance. It must happen by design.

Listen

Communication is as much about listening as it is about talking. For leaders, this means creating opportunities to listen to your constituents. The successful leader understands the importance of making time to listen and to just "be present" for his constituents. But let's face it, we are busy people. Impromptu chat sessions are great when they happen, but for most of us, if we really want to make sure that we are listening carefully, we have to construct processes that will allow for that to happen. When listening is a priority in your culture, you will make sure that it happens.

This is where the Communication Planning Grid comes in. Use it to plan key messages, tactics for delivering those messages and structured time to connect with stakeholders in listening sessions. Check the plan and the implementation regularly to make sure you are doing what you set out to do.

When it comes to customer service, your communication efforts are limited only by your imagination! Keeping customer service front and center in the minds of busy health care employees can be a daunting task. Working out a detailed communication plan can help get them all talking the same customer service language.

For several years I helped conduct new employee orientations for a community hospital. As at most hospitals, orientation involved clinical and non-clinical employees, as well as volunteers. My role in the orientation was to link customer service to the organization's mission, vision and values. In addition to sharing our standards for service excellence, I emphasized that everything we do in health care needs to help raise the patient's level of confidence in us.

I encouraged the new employees to screen their surroundings and their actions through that goal and to continually ask themselves, *"How does this help to raise confidence in us? How do I live out the goals and values of this organization every day?"* It is the little things of each encounter that add up to trust. Every little thing adds up to make a big difference for your patients.

What patients see, hear and experience creates credibility as well as satisfaction with a facility. Trust is built one person at a time, one encounter at a time, with each employee who makes up the health care organization. Encourage each person to evaluate her role to define how it helps to build trust with every patient encounter. Ask your employees, do they treat each person as if she were their mother or other loved one?

Trust takes time to build up - and only moments to be shattered. Look for the extra touches, literally, that can be done to make the patient feel that you and your organization are the best, safest and most competent place to come for care.

Communication is the key to keeping customer service at the top of everyone's priority list. Your customer service team should appoint a communication leader who will be responsible for orchestrating all communications related to customer service. That person is charged with making sure messages are linked to mission, patient satisfaction and action teams.

But all good communication starts with a plan. When you're communicating about customer service, it's crucial to build in the elements of timing and accountability. For those who have multiple priorities, customer service often falls off the list. Department leaders may need a staff person who can help them keep some of the vital information front and center.

In developing your communication plan, make sure to plan ahead at least one to three months into the future so that you're not scrambling at the last minute for something to talk about. Plan out *what* you're going to communicate, *who's* going to do it, *when* it's going to get done, *how* it's going to get done, *how* it is tied to the organizational mission, vision and values, and *why* it's important to your overall customer service strategy.

Lack of planning for communication that's coupled with an enthusiastic customer service team can result in multiple disjointed tactics that can sometimes confuse the audience.

When you're crafting your plan, remember these three keys to keeping customer service front and center: communicate everything, communicate often and communicate distinctively.

Beware of "micromessaging"

One more thing about communication: Beware of "micromessages" that may inadvertently sabotage your best intentions. We've all heard the adage, "Actions speak louder than words." Actions that speak volumes can be as seemingly minor as a glance, a sigh, or the length and firmness of a handshake. In a work setting, these micromessages can be advantageous in promoting optimal performance, or just as damaging when they become micro-inequities. In his book, "Micromessaging - Why Great Leadership is Beyond Word" (2007, McGraw Hill), author Stephen Young taps into one of the most important, yet undervalued, tools of leadership. Young discusses the gestures, facial expressions, tone of voice, and other subtle behaviors that influence relationships, both positively and negatively.

As a leader, your development of a heightened awareness of micromessaging can not only help you to "read" the members of your team, but also to ensure that you are sending the messages that will help you build morale, trust, and productivity.

Young reveals how micromessages are universally understood language that we begin interpreting and using virtually at birth. What I found particularly interesting is the correlation between micromessaging, language, and culture. As language evolved, so did culture. But even without spoken words, micromessaging conveys volumes of information between people demonstrating disapproval, approval, joy, curiosity, and a plethora of other emotions.

In corporate culture, this form of communication often has a great deal to do with how we interact with one another. More often than not, we aren't even aware of the micro-advantages and micro-inequities.

Communication is a vital skill for all leaders, especially when they need to keep priorities clear and visible to all constituents. It takes skill, planning and the sheer desire to help build a greater understanding of the driving force behind the organization.

6. Lead by example.

"Example isn't the main thing, it is the only thing."

- Albert Schweitzer

While the expression "actions speak louder than words" makes perfect sense, it is often the one thing that sabotages all the best-laid plans in an instant.

Our firm was recently asked to help an organization develop a culture of service excellence. One of the first things that we did was to schedule a visioning session with a group of its senior leaders. The group, including two CEOs and 12 senior members, was scheduled for an intense three-hour meeting with us.

At the 1 p.m. start time, however, only one of the CEOs was present, and fewer than half the expected number of executives had shown up. Over the next 20 minutes, more executives wandered in, took their seats and half-heartedly "joined" the meeting. Meanwhile, at least five of the executives in the meeting were sending text messages from their BlackBerries, and one was eating a bag lunch.

During the meeting, the one CEO left to take a call. While he was out, two of the VPs wandered out and then returned. This charade was nothing short of unbelievable, and it was impossible to keep the meeting on task. It was horribly demeaning and disappointing to me as a presenter, but it doesn't take a rocket scientist to understand what was missing here. The missing element, plain and simple, was respect. At one point, we actually stopped and offered to reschedule the meeting, but the CEO insisted that we stay - because, he said, he felt it was important.

After the meeting, I asked to speak privately with the CEO. I brought with me a copy of his organization's three core values, one of which is respect. I asked him to tell me what behaviors he looked for from staff that would demonstrate respect. He quickly rattled off several things. I then asked him to recall our recent meeting and compare his own conduct during that meeting with the expectations that he holds for his staff. Red-faced, he replied that he had failed miserably. We discussed how his staff's behavior mirrored his own and that a lasting culture shift had to begin with his setting the example.

I must admit that I walk the fine line between courage and sheer stupidity when it comes to challenging leaders about their conduct. I always run the risk that they will feel that I crossed the line, but I wouldn't be doing my job if I ignored the obvious. If I feel diminished, I can't imagine how the staff feels if they are this blatantly disrespected.

In this case, the CEO was a class act when it came to admitting his mistake. Not only did he listen respectfully to my blatant criticism, he openly thanked me for being so forthright with him. More than one CEO has told me that no one had ever been that honest with them. As flattering as that may be, it is also sad to think that so few people are willing to speak up and address the issues. I realize that confronting CEOs about their behaviors may not be good for business, but unless we are all willing to challenge one another and hold up a mirror when necessary, we will never be able to bring about the changes that are necessary to achieve excellence.

Walk the talk

If a culture of excellence is truly a priority, that means fostering excellence in working conditions, as well as in the patient experience. I can't tell you how many employee focus groups we have conducted during our culture assessments where staff tell us that they feel pulled, stressed, and discounted. During one focus group, a nursing assistant fought back tears when she told the story of how her manager demanded that every person "make customer service their number one priority." Yet when the nursing assistant pointed out that they didn't have bedside tables, chairs for visitors, or working call lights - some of the most essential tools needed to deliver good service - her manager shot back, "There's nothing in the budget for that. You will have to make do."

That same nursing assistant suggested that I visit their unit during meal times to witness patients eating from meal trays perched precariously on their laps, due to the shortage of bedside tables. I did. And I was appalled. But the experience gave me a great opportunity to talk with the CEO about the mixed messages being sent to managers. Senior leaders were saying that service was the number one priority, but the Budget King was still reigning supreme in the hearts and minds of the managers whose feet were held to the fire throughout the budget cycle.

This example was a jolt of reality for the senior leaders who had to reframe their messages about making resources available where necessary. The senior leaders were stunned to realize that they had unwittingly created a barrier by emphasizing the budget as a greater priority than service.

After hearing this story, the CEO's first impulse was to personally make rounds on all of the units to find out what the staff needed in order to do their jobs better. He told me, "I want to personally see that they are heard and that their needs are fulfilled." Although his plan was well intended, I cautioned him to step back and let his managers take the lead on fulfilling staff needs. I tactfully told him that he couldn't always be the one to ride in on the white stallion to save the day. I suggested that he would be doing far more to foster a healthy change in the culture by positioning his managers as the people most responsive to staff requests.

The CEO's job was to make the priority known to both the managers and staff, ensure that they would get the resources that they needed, then get out of their way. It was important that the staff see that their managers were tuned in and responsive to their requests.

At the same time, it was important for the managers to make sure that the staff felt valued and recognized for making their needs known. As new equipment was purchased, the managers made a point of announcing that this was being done as a result of their input. The resounding message was, "You spoke. We listened. Thank you for making this a better place for our patients and a better place to work."

If you are sincere about your priorities and are willing to do the work necessary to keep those priorities at the top of everyone's minds, then following these steps will help you to stay the course even through the roughest times.

Raising the Bar:
Scripps' clear priorities foster turnaround

Not every hospital has the luxury of a full time physician relations staff. For Carl Etter, CEO of Scripps Memorial Hospital Encinitas, in California, physician relations floated to the top of his list of priorities from the very start of his engagement with Scripps.

Arriving at his post in the California hospital in 2003, Etter was facing a dismal bottom line along with strained physician and staff relations. He knew that in order to turn around the hospital's financial situation, he had to engage the medical staff quickly. But the greatest challenge was a lack of trust, steeped in a long history of damaged relationships between the hospital and medical staff.

The CEO's perspective – Carl Etter:

Having worked in a number of hospitals throughout the country, Etter recognizes the importance of good physician relations. Without it, a hospital cannot be successful. "Experience has taught me that you will make your budget if your doctors support you," he says. "Without physician support, everything from quality to growth and service will be an uphill battle."

Etter knew that if his medical staff and administrative team could collaborate, they would achieve their goals in length of stay, quality, productivity and service excellence. "But collaboration is born of trust, and trust must be earned the old fashioned way – through relationships based on truth and consistent follow-through," he says.

A physician-friendly culture requires that senior leaders be honest and accessible and relate to the medical staff in a spirit of collaboration. "That takes focus," he says. "We had to be able to focus on the physician's needs in order to build trust and credibility with the medical staff. That meant being accessible at all hours and for virtually all the physicians' concerns. They wanted a direct line to the senior executives and needed to know what they were important enough to have my ear any time."

Etter began by identifying the informal leaders within the medical staff to gain important insights from them. "We needed to understand the culture from their perspective and look for truth in order to help them put aside any baggage from the past," he says.

"One of the objectives I had going into the Scripps system was to create a hospitalist program in Encinitas. We needed to make the change in order to provide greater continuity in care, reduce length of stay and manage risk," he says. "In most environments, making this transition can be rife with stress, suspicion and even sabotage. If we wanted to be successful, the doctors had to be on board."

And the physician champions made it happen, he says. "The hospitalists structured their own terms of accountability. They have defined the incentives and have taken a greater stake in the hospital's success."

Among the physician champions is Dr. James Labelle, medical director of quality and emergency services for Scripps Memorial Hospital Encinitas. Labelle has been with Scripps for 20 years, 10 of them in a leadership capacity.

The physician perspective – Dr. James Labelle

Dr. James Labelle has seen a huge shift in his organization since he was chief of staff in 2001. "To summarize the culture, I must say that the administration was weak, and the medical staff was cynical. It was an environment of 'every man for himself,'" he says. "The byproduct was a meltdown of practices."

The environment began to change when a new administrator arrived and began to focus on partnering with physicians: "He made it clear that he wanted to build the best shop for the doctors to work in. He was great at drawing doctors in and helping them to understand what it takes to make a hospital successful and to create a strategy for the future. His priorities for the organization were crystal clear."

The medical staff – "hungry for an honest, open relationship" – embraced the new philosophy with open arms. The leadership team now advises administration on how the medical staff and hospital can work more closely. "The biggest element of change was getting to a place where the hospital leadership and the medical staff had a willingness to listen and trust," he says. "I hadn't experienced this type of transformation before".

The system's CEO, Chris Van Gorder, chose the right man for the job when he appointed Carl Etter as the CEO of Scripps Memorial Hospital Encinitas, says Labelle. "As we developed trust, the medical staff started becoming more engaged. Over time, that engagement has continued to amplify."

Early on, Etter had asked the medical staff to create a list of priorities. "We developed the list of 10 priorities, many of which were dropped firmly into his lap," Labelle says. "In the first year, he executed all of them. That was the turning point for us. As the list was accomplished, the physicians gained more trust and confidence in the hospital leadership. Jointly, we have seen greater successes in financial, quality and individual goals."

Etter also dealt with some cultural issues with the management team. He focused on helping managers relate to physicians. In solving problems, "He delivered a clear and consistent message that we're part of the same team and system, so it is no longer acceptable for doctors to blame nurses, and vice versa," he says. "He taught us that we needed to act quickly to eliminate adversity and create partners with the nursing staff. In hindsight, we can see now that a culture of distrust leads to inaction and drives people farther apart. In contrast, the new culture has encouraged physicians to take on a leadership role."

Trust, he explains, "can't be just words. It must be deeds in action. Of course, we're human and make mistakes, but we've learned not to play blame games. We're more accountable for our own shortcomings now. We address them and move on. The leadership of the hospital and medical staff articulate a common vision that resonates with the physicians."

The organization's physicians no longer feel frustrated and angry because of a lack of control over patient care. "Now, if something is broken, we take ownership to fix it with an open dialogue," he says. "We recognize that we needed a culture shift that included a better hand-off and listen more carefully to nursing."

A new chief nursing officer, Jan Zachry, made even more improvements. "Her open and responsive nature helped to further the trust factor between nursing and physicians. Improved communication has resulted in better patient care," Labelle says. "The physicians are communicating better, and nursing staff has learned how to speak so doctors listen. There have been many tiny things that, when combined, build greater trust. We don't own the hospital legally, but we feel ownership and treat the hospital and staff as partners."

Numerous programs have come out of the organization's medical executive committee, sending the message: "We're trustworthy. We deliver, and this is a priority." Even during times of budget constraints, there was always follow-through, because change was centered on the good of the patient.

Etter's vision of hospital administration and how doctors relate to one another were the crux of the organization's culture shift. "To be honest, we were tough to get along with when he first arrived because we felt like we were at the bottom of the totem pole," admits Labelle. "We didn't feel heard or valued. Once we began to feel like partners and could trust our administration, the culture shifted." With trust, follow-through, shared problem solving and a sense of openness, managers and physicians are partners working together toward a common goal; providing the best care for their patients.

Labelle adds that communication between doctors and nurses has also improved. "Many of the old issues have been resolved," he says, which also leads to better outcomes for patients. And a new alignment between the hospitalists and ED has resulted in a more reasonable length of stay. "That would not have happened without respectful collaboration," says Labelle.

"We're optimistic about our future, but it's hard to predict. I think we need to look less to the inside and more outside of the hospital and focus on how we can support the needs of the community," says Labelle. "As physicians, we have to embrace a partnering culture in that endeavor. We are still independent doctors. We have some basic strategies needed to survive, including pay for performance, public reporting and marketing. We have to stay progressive in order to grow the medical staff and recruit high-quality physicians to serve our community well into the future. We have an obligation to the community to plan ahead to replace ourselves." Discussions on achieving these goals are beginning.

Labelle's one regret is that it took the organization so long to face – and address – the "huge elephant on the table... we should have been talking about the elephant 15 years ago. (Now) we've got a great relationship with system leadership... everyone is rowing in the same direction."

Labelle credits the corporation's Physician Leadership Cabinet, co-chaired by CEO Chris Van Gorder and CMO Dr. Brent Eastman, for giving the medical staff "a voice." As a result, administrators and staff from all five hospitals meet monthly to discuss problems and strategies, dealing constructively with staff issues across the system. "They are truly invested in creating the best workplace for physicians and, ultimately, the best care environment for our patients," says Labelle. "That's a win/win situation."

An outsider's view – Baird Consulting

Measuring success is both qualitative and quantitative. Of course there are surveys indicating greater physician satisfaction, but the softer, qualitative indicators can be equally meaningful when evaluating a culture.

Today, the physicians at Scripps Memorial Hospital – Encinitas are taking a much more active role on multidisciplinary teams and are accountable for helping the hospital to achieve mutual goals. One example of their collaborative spirit is evident in their approach to improving patient satisfaction. When I met with the hospitalists and intensivists to discuss patient satisfaction scores and priorities for improvement, I had a pleasant surprise. I'm accustomed to physicians spending the first hour of our time together trying to "explain away the data." This team moved quickly from denying that they had a problem and onto finding solutions that would make a difference.

It was evident from the start that these physicians were a step ahead in embracing a culture of collaboration with the hospital. There wasn't the finger-pointing and naysaying that is prevalent among most of the medical groups we've worked with. Instead, we found physicians eager to brainstorm how they could make improvements.

Even after the training session ended, many of the physicians stayed on to discuss their action teams and how they would go about making changes needed to improve patient satisfaction scores. Within one week, we learned that several of the physicians had formed service improvement action teams or joined teams on nursing units. Creating a culture of service excellence requires buy-in from the medical staff, as well as support from administration. It was clear from the beginning that this team had the winning combination.

Raising the bar:
Priorities unify Liberty's multiple facilities

What does it look like when a leader commits to making customer service a priority? If I were to paint a picture of what the leadership looks like in an environment of excellence, I'd be very likely to
paint Liberty Lutheran Services of Pennsylvania.

President and CEO Luanne Fisher embarked on her quest for
excellence more than 15 years ago when she visited a Ritz-Carlton
facility. Convinced that if hotels can create world-class service,
health care can as well, Fisher began to rally support for her vision to
apply The Ritz-Carlton philosophy to Liberty Lutheran's long-term
care facilities.

Liberty Lutheran has made service a priority, and it shows. Is
everything perfect? No. Has every goal been achieved? No. "It's still
a work in progress," says Fisher, "particularly since we are still adjust-
ing to the merger of four unique organizations."

Liberty Lutheran Services has more than 90 years of experience
in not-for-profit, faith-based, long-term care. However, it broad-
ened its reach significantly when it brought Lutheran Children and
Family Services under its umbrella of affiliates. Although the organizations serve very different populations, they are united in one
common mission.

I heard Fisher and Christopher Ridenhour, director of Core
Competency Training for Liberty Lutheran Services, speak at an
American Association for Homes and Services for the Aging
(AAHSA) conference in 2007. I was impressed by how well their
organization positioned service excellence as a priority. Several steps
they had taken made their priority crystal clear:

1. They set very clear goals under what Fisher calls their "World
Class Objectives." They strive for excellence in five distinct areas,
including internal and external customer service program innovation, fiscal solvency, and leadership as a faith-based organization.

2. They demonstrate that service is a priority by creating and supporting positions such as the one held by Ridenhour. Ridenhour has helped to define, and train for, service behaviors. Rather than provide a one-shot orientation, Ridenhour helps people to grow and develop continually, and rewards high performers.

3. They foster ongoing education and development. "Education is more than teaching the skills," says Ridenhour. "It is about engaging people in a conversation that speaks to our relationships with one another." Liberty Lutheran starts with four hours of concentrated customer service training and continues with all the core competencies, for a total of 10 training days per year. Most staff attend training for one of the 10 core competencies at least once per month. Allocating resources to training and development is clear evidence that Liberty Lutheran's leaders make service a top priority.

4. Mutual accountability. Staff-level employees are not only expected to abide by the established customer service standards, they are also accountable for such things as knowing who within the organization can help solve customer problems, concerns and needs; seeking out and accepting mentoring from staff with a reputation for excellent customer service; and advising other staff on customer preferences. Supervisors' account-abilities include such things as getting first-hand customer information and using it to improve service, advising staff on how to develop good customer relationships.

All of these elements, when taken together, encompass the organization's commitment to people, process, passion and a connection to purpose. But none of this would have given such sustainable results without clear priority.

In addition to thorough orientation and training, leaders have tied specific accountabilities to each level within the organization. Using job grades to outline the varying levels of responsibilities,

Liberty Lutheran defined what is expected of employees at each level.

For example, managers are expected to coach and mentor staff in customer service best practices, develop and facilitate programs and resolve complaints to meet customer expectations.

Directors are expected to champion customer relations as well as to develop policies that will help to meet and exceed customer expectations.

At the executive level, the expectations are even more expansive. The leaders are expected to create and maintain an environment that will ensure corporate-wide excellence.

According to Ridenhour, "Organizations are a direct reflection of their leadership. There are a lot of leaders out there who are not true to their promises. We are fortunate to have a leader with a clear vision but who also knows that she is one person with one viewpoint. She is open to being challenged on her ideas and actually invites disagreement and challenge. If you are not open to feedback or differences in opinion, an organization cannot possibly realize its potential. The challenge for any leader is learning to strike the balance between the compassionate heart and the analytical mind. We have a leader who can balance compassion with analytics. Our priorities are clear, but she is always open to change."

Leaders who make service a priority face a multitude of challenges. Luanne Fisher is no exception. She emphasizes that one of the most important qualities a leader needs to shift a culture is sheer persistence. "It doesn't happen overnight," she admits, "but setting clear priorities helps get us back on track if we start veering off in the wrong direction."

When asked what she would do differently if she had it to do over again, Fisher says, "Looking back, I realize that I made too many accommodations for individuals' whims and needs. When you have a clear vision and clear priorities, people need to make up their minds to get on the bus or get off."

Leader reflections

Reflect and journal on the following:

- How do you communicate the organizational mission, vision and values?
- How well are you linking the mission and vision to service goals and results?
- How do you determine if the patient experience matches the promises your organization makes?
- What actions do you take to demonstrate that service is a priority to you personally?
- What do you feel you are doing well right now in communicating and demonstrating your priorities?
- How are managers held accountable for cascading communication within their departments?

Actions

- Clarify how well you are setting and communicating priorities.
- Review key messages from the last 30 days. How well do your communications reflect your true priorities?
- What are two or three actions you will take to improve the way you demonstrate service excellence as a priority?
- Name three things that you do to set an example in terms of organizational priorities.
- Identify at least one new tool you can use to communicate organizational priorities more clearly.

Chapter Two

"I've learned that people will forget what you said, people will forget what you did, but people will never forget how you made them feel."

- Maya Angelou

No one will argue that human capital is any service organization's greatest asset. Virtually every bookstore in America has shelves of business publications expounding the merits of growing a solid workforce. Much of the advice found in these books is somewhat universal. The resounding themes are: Hire right, provide adequate training, treat everyone fairly, reward good behavior and correct or eliminate bad behavior.

Simple? Yes. Easy? No. Successful businesses know the value of their work force and continually strive to improve it. Jim Collins is widely recognized for his book, "Good to Great", in which he talks about getting the right people on the bus, in the right seats, and the wrong people off the bus. Collins credits good-to-great leaders with understanding that if they begin with "who" in their business strategies rather than "what," they can more easily adapt to a changing world. Few leaders would argue with Collins' logic, yet many of us are still turning a blind eye to some of our most obvious personnel problems. Even the most seasoned leaders have a hard time facing up to tough personnel decisions.

I have intentionally placed this chapter after the Priority chapter because developing a high-quality work force is by far the most important first step in achieving customer service goals once your priority has been set. After all, it is your people who serve your customers. Get the right ones in place, make sure they know what to do and how to do it, then keep developing them and rewarding them. Why? Because this is the foundation on which everything else rests.

The engagement/loyalty link

Happy, engaged employees are more likely to deliver better service and thus create a better patient experience. Who can argue the logic in that? But we like to see the proof. Numerous studies over the years have validated the correlation between employee satisfaction and patient satisfaction.

According to the "Hospital Check-Up Report" (2007, Press Ganey Associates, Inc.), there is a correlation between employee and patient satisfaction, indicating that high levels of employee satisfaction are associated with high levels of patient satisfaction. In other words, satisfied employees tend to speak well of the hospital outside of work, which can lead to more patient referrals.

Figure 1 displays the patient–hospital employee loyalty link. The extent to which a hospital meets its patients' expectations for care is strongly related to how the hospital's employees feel about their workplace.

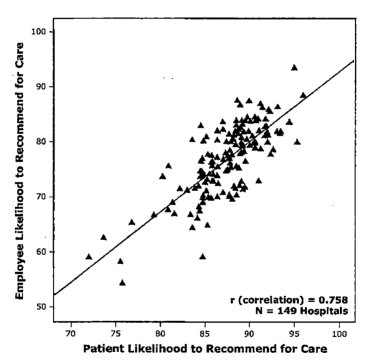

Patient Likelihood to Recommend for Care

An employee's level of engagement has significant implications for health care leaders who want to improve the culture and enhance the patient experience. This leads us to seek a better understanding of what factors most influence employee satisfaction.

In 2006, Press Ganey Associates, Inc. completed a year-long study of 373 health care facilities nationwide. Their research identified the statements on the employee satisfaction survey that were most closely correlated with the question, "How likely are you to recommend this organization to a friend as a good place to work?" The correlations resulted in a priority index ranking all employees' top priorities:

Survey item	Priority rank
Senior Leadership really listens to employees	1
Promotions are handled fairly here	2
Senior leadership can be trusted to be straightforward and honest	3
I am satisfied with my involvement in decision making	4
My work group is asked for opinions before decisions are made	5

Their sample represents the experiences of a total of 193,163 employees (2007 Press Ganey Associates, Inc., *Hospital Check-up Report: Nurse and Employee*).

Nurses in the study demonstrated that three of their top priorities were the same as those identified among all employees. Nurses ranked their priorities as follows:

Survey item	Priority rank
Senior leadership really listens to employees	1
Senior leadership can be trusted to be straightforward and honest	2
Senior leadership responds promptly to most problems	3
I am satisfied with my involvement in decision making	4
Senior leadership is aware of the major concerns of employees	5

Based on this information, it is important that senior leaders consider how they fare in each of the top five categories. You may think you are doing well in these areas, but what do your employees think? Consider these questions:

- If employees rate *Senior leadership really listens* as their number 1 priority, ask yourself how you are demonstrating that you are listening.
  - * Action step: When you take action based on employee feedback, connect the dots. Tell them, "You spoke and we listened. Here is what we did."
- What actions are you taking to demonstrate that you are straightforward and honest?

* Action step: Demonstrate that you are committed to transparency. Don't just make an announcement; tell employees that you want them to be the first to know breaking news. The more you can do to be transparent, the better. Managers and supervisors need to echo this message repeatedly when passing along information within their departments. Script announcements and talking points, using words that demonstrate straightforward information.
- How are you involving employees in decision making? When you do involve employees in decision-making, how do you let other employees know there has been grass-roots input and involvement?
  * Action step: Publish the names of team members working on improvements. In the departments, show photos of the teams and acknowledge how individuals and teams are involved in decisions.

Listening and taking action

If you know that employees want senior leaders who really listen, it's important to examine your behaviors in light of that issue.

A few years ago, my firm was called in to help a mid-sized medical practice that was experiencing high employee turnover and dismal patient satisfaction ratings. They wanted us to help them shift the culture to a more service-centered environment. After doing some mystery shopping and conducting in-depth interviews with the physicians and staff, one glaring problem became crystal clear; the manager was an absolute tyrant. She was a control monger who ruled with an iron fist and burned through staff like tissue paper in a bonfire. She was known for publicly berating employees and throwing infantile temper tantrums. When I pointed these problems out to the medical director and CEO of the practice, he told me, quite emphatically, "We would never fire her. She has been with us since day one. She's our anchor."

Now, I will give you my disclaimer right out front. I am not a psychologist, and I should probably not throw around psychiatric diagnoses loosely, but I have seen my share of co-dependent relationships between physicians and their nurses and managers, and this one was a classic. The physicians had grown to depend on the manager, and she, in turn, had managed to convince them that she was indispensable and, therefore, untouchable. This manager felt as secure as any animal on the endangered species list, yet, her staff described her as impossible to work for.

During employee and physician interviews I learned that the physician leaders would dismiss employee complaints about the manager and advise them to speak with her directly about any problems. The physicians felt that by doing this, they were helping employees to follow the chain of command. The result was employees feeling that senior leaders were not listening and were not responsive to their needs, so they would simply leave their positions.

The "anchor" that the physicians described was not a positive, stabilizing force, but rather a heavier weight that was holding them down and putting them at risk for drowning in the muck and mire of turnover and poor patient satisfaction.

I got the physicians' attention when I pointed out the cost of turnover - not only in terms of recruiting and training, but in the lack of continuity in patient care. Yet they still insisted on giving the manager another chance. The caveat was that they would personally conduct all exit interviews over the next six months. As expected, the turnover didn't change, nor did the patient satisfaction improve, until the physicians decided to terminate the manager. It was only then that they could begin the process of healing among the remaining staff, building buy-in, and turning the culture into a more open, innovative and customer-centered environment.

Terminating problem employees isn't easy, even when you know it is the right thing to do. I am always reminding leaders of this simple truth: Every day you allow problem employees to remain on your payroll is one more day they are eroding your credibility - and the credibility of the entire mission, vision and priorities of your organization.

You may proclaim that you value a service-centered culture, but the reality is that your employees are watching your actions more closely than they are listening to your words. The consequence for keeping problem employees with undesirable behavior is that they collect a paycheck every two weeks, exactly like your star performers. What message does that send? Money, and the security it brings, is a form of reward. When you allow marginal performers to remain on the payroll, it sends the message that you don't really mean what you say about valuing a service-centered culture.

Don't pass the trash!

"Passing the trash" is one of health care's dirty little secrets. I have seen it in virtually every organization with which I have worked as either an employee or a consultant.

What is passing the trash? It is that covert practice of quietly passing the marginal performers on to other departments and breathing a sigh of relief when you can say they are no longer your problem. No one likes to admit that they do this, and yet, you will see the same scene played out over and over again, from organization to organization.

What amazes me is that this dirty little practice happens even among managers who call themselves team players and friends! These managers wouldn't dream of taking a bag of hazardous waste and dropping it inside another department, yet this is exactly what is being done when we pass along the problem workers who erode the morale of our other team members, drag down our patient satisfaction scores, and irritate us to the point of distraction.

It takes commitment from the entire management team to stop this practice in the name of culture enhancement and optimal performance. And it takes the full support of senior leaders to stand behind the managers in making the tough decisions.

Face it, most of us don't like confrontation. We'd much rather invest our energies elsewhere. Avoidance behavior may be human nature, but it almost never serves us well in the long run. And for leaders, avoiding uncomfortable performance discussions only erodes your team's trust in you. The high performers have to do double duty to make up for the low performers' shortcomings. At the same time, these high performers witness your allowing the marginal performers to collect a paycheck and the same benefits that they do.

And these are only the surface issues. Beneath the surface, the disengaged employee is not just marginally productive, he or she is often toxic to morale. These are the people who are negative about the department, the organization and everything around them. They help perpetuate the "us versus them" mentality that keeps the department and the organization from achieving and sustaining a culture of service excellence. They are hurting you and everyone around them.

In a healthy culture of accountability, managers don't pass the trash. They deal with it. That means clarifying expectations, coaching, disciplining, and documenting in order to do what is necessary to create and sustain a high-performing team. I'm all for giving people a fair chance. But when you have made your expectations clear to your marginal performers and have made sure they know what to do and how to do it, it's up to them to take action to improve their performance. And ultimately, it is up to the manager to decide whether they stay or go.

In his book, "Hardwiring Excellence" (2003, Firestarter Publishing), author and well-known customer service expert, Quint Studer, talks about the low, middle and high performers within the organization. Studer recommends that leaders re-recruit middle and high performers to help foster further growth and to reaffirm their value to the organization. At the same time he recommends isolating the low performers and engaging them in discussions that will either help them move their performance up to a middle or high level, or out of the organization altogether.

In my 30 years in health care, I've learned that leadership is not for the faint of heart. It takes guts to make the right decisions for your team, but once you do, the rewards are palpable. And with experience, leaders will find it much less difficult to spot the problems and deal with them swiftly. When your staff sees that you mean business, they will have greater respect for you, and will trust that service really is a priority throughout the entire organization.

No one ever gets fired here!

During organizational culture assessments, my colleague Kevin Stranberg and I conduct focus groups with employees to determine how they view the culture and to identify potential barriers to service excellence. Several times over the years, employees have told us, "No one ever gets fired here." They go on to tell us horror stories similar to the one above, laced with tales of tyrants and bullies who have not only been allowed to collect a paycheck, but who have often been placed in supervisory or management positions. For organizations that are on a quest for excellence, this cannot be allowed to persist. If it does, the high-performing, engaged staff will become increasingly disillusioned with the gap and either leave or shift their talents to other personal pursuits.

In his book, "The No Asshole Rule" (2007, Warner Business Books), Robert Sutton lays it squarely on the line for leaders who have turned a blind eye to the bullies and jerks on the payroll. This author is much bolder than I would be in using the term "asshole," but he does a great job of shedding light on a problem that sucks the life out of the work place. He lists the "Dirty Dozen - Common Every Day Actions That Assholes Use:"

1. Personal insults
2. Invading one's personal territory
3. Uninvited physical contact
4. Threats and intimidation, both verbal and nonverbal
5. "Sarcastic jokes" and "teasing" used as insult delivery systems
6. Withering e-mail flames
7. Status slaps intended to humiliate their victims
8. Public shaming or "status degradation" rituals
9. Rude interruptions
10. Two-faced attacks
11. Dirty looks

12. Treating people as if they are invisible

Sutton describes the cost of allowing jerks to infiltrate your organization. In addition to zapping the energy of others around the problem employee, Sutton describes some very tangible costs in his summary, "What's your TCA? Factors to Consider when Calculating the Total Cost of Assholes to your Organization" (Sutton, p. 49-51).

Engagement: the catalyst for improvement

Virtually every health care organization in the world will say they want a powerful patient experience, yet relatively few of us have made a conscious connection between having a powerful patient experience and having a powerful employee experience. Most of us are sucked into the vicious cycle of recruitment and hiring and not spending enough time and energy on engaging our employees to deliver the patient experience we know is possible. I frequently see evidence of this in organizations that willingly spend $50,000 to $100,000 on recruitment campaigns, but invest little to nothing on culture-enhancing strategies. To break this vicious cycle, we need to start thinking and acting in a way that increases the level of employee engagement. When employees are more engaged, they will stay longer and become beacons of light that draw new talent to the organization.

The Center for Talent Retention (CTR), in Denver, Colorado, has identified 50 "drivers" that cause employees to engage and perform - as well as to stay. Whether consciously or subconsciously, employees make decisions to engage or disengage. Similarly, they decide to stay or leave. These internal decisions have an impact on how the employees treat the patient and the patient's family, and ultimately influence the entire patient experience. Using these 50 drivers, CTR has developed a system to help managers get a quick understanding of what is most crucial in engaging and keeping talent.

"It's not enough to simply measure employee satisfaction," says

Cindy Mustful, vice president for the Center for Talent Retention. "Satisfaction will only get you so far ... Engaged and fully engaged employees contribute a significant amount of their time, energy, and talent to making their department and the organization the best that it can be."

Engagement is defined as the productive use of an individual's ideas, talents and energy. Engagement influences what employees do, what results they produce, and how they affect those around them. When you can increase an employee's level of engagement, you can improve his or her productivity and, ultimately, patient satisfaction. By understanding their employees' current levels of engagement, health care leaders can work to move them to higher levels of engagement.

Using a practice called "Engagement Planning," developed by CTR, managers compare what their direct reports do, the results they deliver, and their impact on others, against the four levels of engagement (Fully Engaged, Engaged, Somewhat Engaged, and Disengaged). They then classify each report into one of the levels. After that step, managers take a look at their team and identify who they think can be moved up a level in the next six months, after taking specific actions. Managers can make a significant difference in engagement by taking specific actions with individuals to increase engagement. Similarly, managers can have a significant impact when they take action to move the disengaged out of the organization.

"Our mantra," says Mustful, "is 'without action, we have nothing.' It's not enough to understand the problems or concerns impacting your ability to engage and retain talent. You have to be able to outline and execute an actionable plan for keeping the 'Fully Engaged' and 'Engaged' employees from backsliding and, at the same time, increase the engagement of anyone who falls into the 'Somewhat Engaged' or 'Disengaged' levels."

"It's important for leaders to understand that employees choose to engage, as well as to stay or leave," emphasizes CTR's CEO, Derrick Barton. "When managers understand this is a choice driven by how well an employee's most critical needs are met in their current work situation, they can then focus on identifying what they will do to increase employee engagement, and ultimately, the patient experience. Developing a plan to increase engagement increases the probability you will take action and work on the areas which will make a difference to get the kind of results you want."

CTR has demonstrated quantifiable performance and financial impacts from having "Disengaged" and "Somewhat Engaged" employees. These are the people who are barely squeaking by in performance and who spend more time distracting others and eroding morale than they do contributing to the patient experience or the bottom line. Unfortunately, these people demand so much coaching that many managers would rather not deal with them. Other pressing priorities take precedence, and the "Disengaged" often fly under the radar or are tolerated because we are too overwhelmed, distracted or lazy to take the necessary actions.

Using specific organizational data on salaries and number of employees, CTR calculates the bottom-line impact of disengaged employees on an organization. I attended a seminar in which actual employee statistics were plugged into the CTR formula for measuring the impact of engagement. I was astounded to see financial ramifications to an organization when even 5 percent (one in 20) of their employees fall into the "Disengaged" and 15 percent (one in seven) are in the "Somewhat Engaged" categories.

If we think about it, most of us can easily classify our staff into one of four categories, according to their level of engagement, as manifested by observable behaviors that can be tied to how they interact with coworkers and patients. I must admit that I winced a little at classifying employees for this exercise. I felt like I was pigeonholing people. But once I got past my initial reaction, I could clearly see that by making this classification, I was setting the stage for an action plan that would benefit not only the employee, but the department, the organization, and, ultimately, the patient experience.

Engagement Level Descriptions

Engagement Level	Engagement Level Definition	On-the-job Performance	TAKE ACTION... Increase engagement level
Level 4 **Fully** **Engaged**	• Passionate about their work and the organization • Will do what ever it takes to deliver results • Feels like a true owner • Delivers consistent, high quality results is their trademark • Finds innovative solutions to the toughest problems • Seen as a role model and leader	**122%** 22% Gain!	When Mgrs. take action... they can keep about 100% "Fully Engaged"
Level 3 **Engaged**	• Focused on their deliverables, project, and individual responsibilities • Delivers good, solid performance • Always does their fair share of work • Works well with others and will help out when asked	**100%**	When Mgrs. take action... they can get about 1-in-5 to increase up to "Fully Engaged"
Level 2 **Somewhat** **Engaged**	• Selective about where they put their energy • Spends a lot of time doing things that are not helping customers or the organization • Delivers when they have to, or when you are watching • Does what it takes to get by • A "Master" at distracting others	**75%** 25% Loss!	When Mgrs. take action... they can get about 1-in-2 to increase to "Engaged"
Level 1 **Disengaged**	• Only works when they have to, they really want to be doing something else • Results are NOT meeting the standard • Has a "We"—"They" perspective • Negative about the organization, as well as in their interactions with coworkers and customers	**55%** 45% Loss!	When Mgrs. take action... they can get about 1-in-10 to "Engaged"

Using the table above, consider the employee behaviors described under the Engagement Level Definition column. As you read through the definitions, you may be able to picture people in your organization that fit those descriptions perfectly. With these individuals in mind, ask yourself how your patients would rate them in the survey category, *responsiveness to concerns and complaints*. Chances are very good that your patients would rate them in the same order in which they are listed. The "Disengaged" would score the lowest and the "Fully Engaged" would score the highest.

Imagine this scenario:

Mrs. Walker switches on her call light and complains that her room is too cold. Based on the descriptions above, imagine how employees at different levels of engagement would respond.

Disengaged Employee - A Disengaged Employee would behave in the following manner:

- Walk into Mrs. Walker's room, snap off the call light and simply say, "Yes...?"
- Look at the thermostat, shrug and say, "It looks okay to me."
- Say, "They never fix these things. We complain to them all the time."

Somewhat Engaged Employee - A Somewhat Engaged employee would behave in the following manner:
- Walk into Mrs. Walker's room and ask, "How can I help you?"
- Adjust the thermostat and say, "That should do it."
- Give the patient the number for maintenance and suggest that Mrs. Walker call them for help if it doesn't warm up.

Engaged Employee - An Engaged employee would:
- Knock on Mrs. Walker's door, wait to be acknowledged and enter. She would turn off the call light, introduce herself and ask how she can help.
- Say, "I'm sorry you are cold. Let me get you another blanket and then I'll check the thermostat."
- Check the thermostat and adjust it if necessary. Make a note to talk with maintenance.
- Tell Mrs. Walker, "I've turned your thermostat up about five degrees. It will take a while to kick in. Please let us know if this isn't warm enough for you."

Fully Engaged Employee - A Fully Engaged employee would behave in the following manner:
- Knock on Mrs. Walker's door, wait to be acknowledged and enter. Upon entering she would introduce herself and ask how she can help.
- Check the thermostat and adjust it.
- Inform Mrs. Walker, "I've turned up your thermostat. It may take a little while to warm up in here. I will check back with you in about 20 minutes to make sure it is working, but in the meantime, I can get you a warm blanket, some socks and another blanket for

your shoulders."

- Return promptly with two warm blankets and some socks.
- Before leaving the room, say, "Is there anything else I can do for you? I have time."
- Check back with Mrs. Walker in 20 minutes. If the temperature is still not satisfactory, call maintenance to report the problem and ask how soon they will be able to adjust the thermostat.
- Tell Mrs. Walker that she has called maintenance and expects someone to be here to adjust the thermostat within 15 minutes.
- Ask Mrs. Walker if there is anything else she would like to make her more comfortable in the meantime.

Which one of these employees would you want to care for you? How would you score each of them on a satisfaction survey?

Most leaders will admit that they have "Disengaged" and "Somewhat Engaged" staff, yet they refrain from taking action, then wonder why patient satisfaction levels don't change. Our own avoidance behavior poses the greatest threat to patient loyalty, employee retention and, ultimately, the organization's reputation.

Organizations that are committed to excellence will also commit to processes that attract employees who are the right fit and continually invest in retention and engagement strategies. The CTR Talent Performance Model below shows the connection between the factors that cause an employee to join, engage and stay in an organization. At the same time, it demonstrates how continuously improving the work force environment will enhance productivity, efficiency and overall quality.

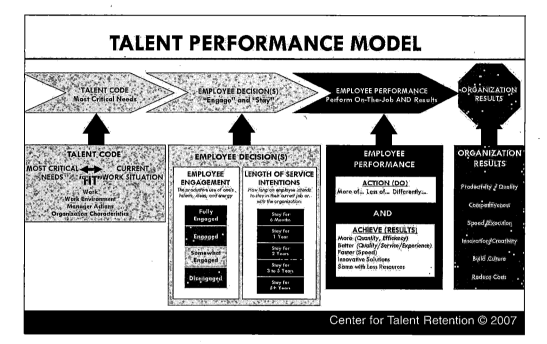

Choose the right fit

Many of our employee problems begin with our hiring practices. We review applications, training, skills and competencies but often don't ask candidates about what is most important to them. Imagine asking an employee about *his* needs as a step in the interview process. Having that information up front, you can match candidates to opportunities based on their identified needs. That way, candidates clearly know what they are walking into and what they can expect.

CTR has developed the Organization FIT Interview Process that helps managers to make sound hiring decisions and, at the same time, raise the level of engagement among their work force. By focusing their attention on hiring for the best fit, managers can avoid the revolving door phenomenon of rapid turnover, particularly during the first year of employment. Employers can develop a clear, compelling, and distinctive way of describing what they have to offer when they know what is most important to job candidates. By the same token, by understanding what is of greatest importance to existing staff, leaders can take specific steps to help them become more engaged and stay.

With the Organization FIT Interview Process, job candidates review a list of "Talent Variables" and identify 10 that are most crucial to causing them to join, engage, and stay within an organization. By understanding the candidates' needs, the employer can strive to match each candidate with a position in context of the real work environment. According to Barton, "This gives the employer the opportunity to sell a position that is a good match or manage expectations in a situation that may not be an ideal fit. Either way, the process provides a rich, robust discussion with candidates about their most crucial needs, even before an offer is on the table."

Using the Organizational Fit Process developed by the Center for Talent Retention, St. Luke's Episcopal Health System in Houston, Texas, managed to cut nurse turnover significantly. When comparing turnover during the year preceding the FIT process with the year following its implementation, St. Luke's documented a 50 percent decrease in nurse turnover. The focus on a solid fit during the hiring process helped them to learn what variables were most critical to the applicants and then to match each person with the position, department and manager that most closely fit those needs.

Hiring right won't fix everything, but it will significantly improve your chances for creating a more positive work environment. The problem is that in health care, we need to have clinically competent individuals to ensure patient safety. This has led us to focus more on clinical and technical skills rather than interpersonal skills.

In the past, we could say that it was just too hard to know if someone had the right personality. After all, how much could you tell in a one-hour interview? But in the past several years, the trend toward behavior-based interviewing has helped employers decipher many of the personality traits that often didn't surface during the more traditional interviews. I am an advocate for behavior-based interviewing because it gives the employer a chance to assess how the candidate responds to questions that delve into their responses to problems. Behavior-based interviewing will help you identify individuals who share your values.

Using standards in the behavior-based interviewing

In my book, "Customer Service in Health Care", I discussed the importance of establishing clear, behavior-based standards for service excellence. By doing so, you are establishing the baseline for your service expectations. I also advocated for including high-performing employees in the crafting of standards. This grassroots approach lends instant credibility to the standards and helps to build ownership from the start.

This level of staff involvement helps people to understand that you recognize their internal best and want to tap into their expertise to build greater consistency. Your service standards help bring your vision to life through specific, expected behaviors. That stage of customer service sets the bar for service excellence. If you have established and upheld the standards you can raise the bar even higher by incorporating these standards in your hiring practices.

Once you have established service standards, use them as a guide to craft behavior-based interview questions. Rather than asking about technical skills that you can often see on the resume, you can learn a lot about how well candidates handle service challenges when you ask them to recap prior experiences. For instance, you can request that the candidate "give an example of a time when you had to deal with an angry patient."

Susan Aloi, MPA, FAMPE, has held health care leadership positions for more than 13 years. Formerly with Columbia University Medical Center in New York, and now with the

University of Utah Medical Group, Aloi has been on the front lines of hiring, coaching, and managing medical practice staff and has an unwavering passion for service excellence. She and I have co-presented customer service training sessions for medical practice executives over the years and share many similar ideas about how to create and sustain a culture of excellence.

Aloi has done a great job of incorporating behavior-based interviewing into her administrative roles over the past several years. After she began measuring patient satisfaction, she realized that she needed a better match between candidates and the positions that had the greatest amount of patient interaction.

According to Aloi, "Medical practices often struggle with turnover in certain jobs and positions where salaries are low and the positions don't require formal education. Positions such as reception, registration and billing don't pay very well, therefore it is tough to attract high-caliber candidates. The candidate pool is often limited and, yet, these people are often the ones who provide patients with their first and most indelible impressions. They are the gatekeepers to the physicians, the keepers of the schedules and the employees who handle numerous patient inquiries about bills. They can make or break the patient relationship, yet we were spending little time filling these positions. We needed to identify and engage the ones with the best people skills.

"Any individual who is dealing with patients, physicians or co-workers," Aloi continues, "needs to be able to demonstrate the most desirable behaviors. That's why we developed questions and anchors that capture crucial touch points."

For example, when Aloi wants to identify someone who goes beyond the basic job duties to meet a patient's needs, she asks candidates to "describe a time when you had to accommodate the special needs of a patient."

"Then we review the candidate's response to look for anchors that would indicate that they 'get it' and know how to accommodate the patient's special needs," she says. "In this case, I am looking for someone who goes outside the prescribed job duties without being asked. I want job candidates to show me that they can think outside the box. A candidate may tell me that her job description is to answer phones, but once, when returning from lunch, she spotted a lost, elderly patient and took the time to find a wheelchair and personally deliver that patient to his destination. She might explain that although it caused her to return late from lunch, she had done what was needed to meet the patient's needs. This type of answer is an anchor that indicates that this candidate thinks on her feet and does what is best for the patient regardless of the job description."

Aloi says she usually develops a series of open-ended interview questions based on specific service standards. In order to grade the candidates' answers, she developed a list of anchors to flag the most desirable responses.

"I realized that when we interviewed for managers and supervisors, we put a lot of thought into it, but we just didn't do that for the front-line people who had so much patient contact," Aloi admits. "We asked ourselves, 'How can we raise the bar on our screening techniques and apply them in a way that will stick?' We needed to make sure we had the best match between the job duties and the personality. That doesn't mean that someone has to be fired if they aren't an ideal fit. They might just need to be re-positioned.

"For instance, I had gotten complaints that one of my staff members was too abrupt on the phone when patients called with billing questions," Aloi recalls. "Her performance showed that she was great at collections, but didn't have the sensitivity to communicate well with patients. She was like a pit bull. This approach might be okay when dealing with the insurance companies, but it just won't work when dealing with patients. We moved her to a position where she wasn't in direct contact with patients anymore and things worked out just fine."

Fostering a culture of excellence requires that managers reinforce the desired behaviors. "I don't want an office manager who chastises an employee for going beyond their job description to serve a patient," says Aloi. "Nor do I want managers to keep staff tied to their desks. I want managers who demonstrate that they embrace a service philosophy and reward and recognize the behaviors we want to foster. So when I hire managers, I ask behavior-based questions that will indicate how they have managed and coached others in order to bring out service-minded behaviors."

Since implementing behavior-based interviewing techniques, Aloi has noticed that she has a much better track record in identifying service-focused candidates. It has also helped her recognize that more time and attention are needed to orient new hires to the culture and philosophy of a service-driven organization. An applicant "may have great skills but may never have been introduced to a service-centered philosophy," she explains. "If I identify a strong skill set in someone who has moderate interpersonal skills, I may hire them and then train them carefully on our culture and philosophy so they are very clear about our expectations and how they will be held accountable. Educating and coaching new hires on the patient-centered philosophy is a vital part of orientation. We need to help them understand that this is how we do things around here. We have a responsibility to educate and model the desirable behaviors, then hold (employees) accountable."

Aloi has some words of advice for managers: "There has to be real accountability for customer service. Managers cannot get into the blame game or shrug their shoulders and say 'It's not my fault' when there are customer service problems. Managers need to hold themselves accountable first and foremost. Then they need to hold everyone else accountable. It starts with behavior-based interviewing for identifying and hiring the best candidates. From there, they need to carry the desirable customer service behaviors over into job descriptions and performance appraisals. In other words, hire right, be clear about your expectations, then reward and recognize employees for performing according to the standards. It all has to fit together."

She adds: "Managers also have to coach their staff every day to hold staff accountable. The first step is to identify the best candidates, get them adequately oriented into the practice, and support them; then reward, recognize and hold every person accountable. And above all, you have to be consistent."

Not every hiring experience is a success, and a manager has to be able to terminate an employee who just doesn't fit the culture and philosophy of service excellence.

"We had an employee once who had the right technical skills and was actually a nice person," Aloi recalls. "She was a good fit with the organization when we hired her for medical records, but in her role she was dealing with referring physicians and patients who were looking for medical records or films. She was incredibly organized and really got the job done efficiently, but when we started getting complaints from patients about her rough and abrupt phone manners, we started to monitor her more closely. We observed her discussions on the phone and were shocked to realize that her phone skills were awful. She was very curt with callers, to the point of being downright rude. Her behavior was just not appropriate in dealing with patients. We tried coaching her in order to improve her phone skills, but in her mind this behavior was needed to get the job done. She felt that she needed to be rough and tough. We had to let her go, because she irritated people. Some of the physicians were furious about her dismissal, but it was necessary. Terminating her sent a clear message to the rest of the staff that we won't tolerate rude behavior in the name of efficiency.

"In that case," Aloi admits, "we had made a bad hire. The lesson we learned was to delve deeper into the questions that would be more apt to reveal attitudes. We also had to look at our practices for monitoring people's phone interactions and evaluate our phone etiquette and skills training.

"There can be a real attitude of complacency in some organizations," Aloi says. "In some cultures, people think that when they are hired, they are set for life. It is important that they see that bad behavior won't be accepted, no matter how long they have been with the organization. As leaders, we need to realize that we are placing a high level of responsibility on the staff that are making $23,000 per year. Their wages are among the lowest, but our practice has so much at stake on them.

"I've seen environments where there had been little or no focus on customer service because there had been no accountability tied to behavior," Aloi says. "There was no standard against which people and performance were measured. When we started measuring and reporting patient satisfaction, we had a clearer indication that job descriptions and hiring practices needed to focus on the interpersonal side, as well as technical skills. As leaders, that meant we needed to engage and identify the best."

"I try to stress that everyone - I mean everyone - can make progress toward customer service improvement regardless of their resources. I don't like to hear, 'We can't give better service because we have limited staff, limited space, or limited time.' I don't allow my team to say we don't have the resources. We can't let these become barriers to success," says Aloi. "Progress is a series of baby steps. I tell my staff, 'Give me an hour a week, and we can do this.' If you let them hide behind the barriers, we can never improve."

Although hiring the next warm body may appear to be the most expeditious route to filling vacancies, the ultimate effect on the organization can be detrimental. Take the time to hire for the best fit and follow up with new hires after 30, 60 and 90 days to find how the experience is going for them. Determine if they have what they need to do their jobs and see if they have any suggestions for making the organization better. New employees provide a fresh set of eyes and perspective. Take the opportunity to learn from these people. They have a wealth of information and insight to share.

Leadership roles & job descriptions

When we ask people, "Whose job is it to deliver great customer service?" The answer we typically hear is, "Everyone's." While that may be true at some level, it is also too simplistic an answer. The real duties associated with building a culture of excellence can be more clearly defined by positions within the organization. When we work with health care organizations, we define the responsibilities as follows:

Position	Senior leaders (CEO, vice presidents)	Directors	Managers	Supervisors (leads, charge nurses)	Staff
Key Role	Establish a strong foundation with compelling vision for excellence	Support and champion service excellence	Lead, structure and coach for service behaviors	Guide and coach for service behaviors	Learn, understand and apply standards in their daily work
Supporting Actions	• Creates and communicates a clear vision for excellence. • Ties service to strategic plan. • Fosters an environment of innovation. • Ensures that resources are available to build processes and innovation linked to excellence. • Understands and communicates a compelling business position for service excellence. • States goals and holds everyone accountable for achieving goals.	• Plans and directs the business unit to meet and exceed customer expectations. • Understands customer service from the stakeholder perspective. • Directs business unit with specific, measurable service goals. • Serves as a sponsor for teams to ensure that they have the resources needed to complete projects. • Seeks industry best practices and applies to internal systems. • Holds departments accountable.	• Keeps customer service initiative visible in the department. • Acquires patient satisfaction data, complaints and commendations. Uses this information to improve department processes. • Rewards and recognizes staff. • Trains and coaches supervisors and staff. • Supports and encourages innovation. • Provides appropriate, timely feedback. Supports and encourages peer recognition.	• Incorporates service standards in training and coaching. • Helps others to understand and apply the service standards in customer interactions. • Supports and encourages innovation and team activity. • Provides appropriate, timely recognition. • Encourages staff to engage in peer recognition activities.	• Takes responsibility for learning and applying the service standards in all encounters. • Identifies ways to apply innovation to problem-solving. • Is an active participant in recognizing peers. • Participants in service improvement training and activities.

Growing your people through coaching

Coaching is among the most important skills that any leader can possess. It simply isn't enough to be a knowledgeable clinician in order to lead a high performing team. You must also be able to help maximize human potential. That, in a nutshell, is what coaching is all about.

As coaches, we play such an important role. Every time we help someone else to achieve their personal best, we are directly and indirectly changing lives.

Every time we coach someone on our team, and that person does one thing to improve the patient experience, we're making a difference. Every encouraging word to staff members who are putting forth their best effort is an incentive for them to do more of the same. Similarly, every time we correct behaviors that threaten to erode patient trust, we are making a monumental difference, because every patient encounter is an opportunity for us to raise their trust in us - or quickly, and often irrevocably, destroy that trust. As health care leaders, you have the power to make those changes, one encounter at a time.

It doesn't matter whether or not we have direct patient contact. Our role, particularly when we focus on coaching, gives us the chance to make a significant difference in the lives of the people we serve.

When you think of the word "coach," what comes to mind? A guy in a sweat suit, clipboard in hand, and a whistle in his mouth? I'm from Green Bay Packers country, so when you mention great coaches, Vince Lombardi holds my top-of-the-mind position. Lombardi has been recognized as one of the greatest coaches of the century, not only for his winning record but for his infectious enthusiasm and spirit. Lombardi was known not only as a great coach, but as a great leader. He said, "The achievements of an organization are the results of the combined efforts of each individual." Isn't that why you are reading this book? You want your organization to be its best. And that hinges on maximizing the performance of each individual.

Coaches can be found everywhere. They come in a variety of settings and with myriad appearances. Some carry the title of coach; others carry related titles like teacher, mentor, preceptor, manager, or supervisor. Do you see yourself in a coaching role? Even if it is not part of your title or job description, as a leader, you are surrounded by coaching opportunities on a daily basis.

I learned the value of coaching skills at very young age. I am the sixth in a family of 10 children. As you can imagine, my mother had her hands pretty full keeping everyone in diapers, shoes, and three square meals a day. She lovingly refers to our clan as a small non-profit organization. With a family this size, it was up to all of us to pitch in as a team to get things done. In big families, children don't have the one-on-one interactions between parent and child that is typical of smaller families. So it isn't always the parents on the front lines of major milestones; it's often your siblings.

When I think about major milestones and accomplishments from my childhood, I fondly remember the coaching and encouragement of my older brothers and sisters. We learned a lot of things from each other, but I have very distinctive memories of crossing important milestones with the help of some of my best "coaches." My sister, Kathi, sat for what seemed like hours with me teaching me to tie my shoes. She was patient and encouraging, but firm, insisting that I could do it. She slowly demonstrated the steps, but then untied the laces so I could repeat the process. Kathi had a natural instinct for helping me tackle fine motor skills. It's no surprise that she became an occupational therapist.

My brother, Tim, taught me to ride a two-wheeled bike. I remember being ready to give up after a few nasty scrapes. Tim pushed me to keep trying when things got tough. He reminded me that any real achievements take practice and perseverance through the setbacks. He even confessed that he had taken a few bad spills himself before he got the hang of it. He encouraged me to pick myself up, dust myself off, and get back on the bike. There's no doubt as to why today, he is a successful CEO who has had to pick himself up after more than a few setbacks.

But the one sibling who taught me the most about the importance of coaching was my younger sister Patty. When Patty was born, my parents spent months going through medical evaluations to find out why she wasn't developing normally. After numerous doctors and tests, my parents were informed by the experts that Patty was mentally retarded. It was 1960, and at that time, the doctors didn't give my parents much hope. In fact, they told my parents, with a degree of certainty, that Patty would never be able to even sit up by herself. These respected medical experts told my parents that in fairness to their other children, Patty should be placed in an institution. When my parents refused, one physician coldly told them, "I suppose you could keep her. Some people find that they make nice pets."

My parents were heartbroken, but believed that with love, encouragement, and stimulation, Patty might just surprise them. And she did. Every phase of Patty's development became a triumph for all of us. Our goal as a family was to help Patty achieve her personal best, whatever that was. We had no idea what she could do, but we knew we wanted her to reach her maximum potential.

I was only 5 years old at the time, but I can still vividly remember the day Patty took her first steps. I remember, because I was one of her coaches. I learned that if I wanted Patty to do something, I had to:

1. Get her attention,
2. Give her an incentive,
3. Encourage her,
4. Soothe her when she stumbled but not coddle and pamper her so that she wouldn't get up and try again or feel sorry for herself,
5. Reward her progress.

So, with the help of a stack of Oreo cookies, I coached her through her wobbly first steps. It was such a feat that I called everyone around to witness this milestone. There, in our living room, and encircled by all of us, Patty took those first tentative steps. We stood back, holding our breath until one wobbly, uncertain step was followed by another, then another. We were so thrilled that we all started clapping and cheering. Patty too, got so caught up in the excitement that she sat right down and cheered for herself. She taught us not only the importance of perseverance in the face of adversity but the simple pleasures of celebrating success and taking pride in achievements.

Patty's life journey hasn't been an easy road. But each milestone, while often a struggle, became a triumph celebrated with much greater appreciation than if she had been born with greater intellectual advantages.

Against the medical odds, Patty grew up, graduated from high school and attended a vocational training program. That training program placed her as a dishwasher at the Fireside Dinner Theater in Fort Atkinson, Wisconsin. It was while working there she met her husband, Ernie. Patty and Ernie continue to inspire us and teach us about the value of maximizing human potential. So, rather than depriving her nine brothers and sisters of parental time and attention, Patty has really enriched all of our lives.

And it's no different for any of us in leadership positions who engage in coaching. Every time you help someone else to become their personal best, you are improving not only their lives but the lives of those around them - including your own.

What is coaching? More than anything else, coaching is about growing people. Growing people results in a better culture. And when you talk about a better culture in health care, you're talking about a better patient experience, and about achieving goals and living the mission, vision and values. With all that said, coaching is one of the most important roles you play as a leader.

High Performing Teams require planning, coaching and feedback. Planning starts with articulating the vision and priorities for your team and setting out the game plan. Then, coaching is needed to align human performance with the vision and game plan. And, last, there is the need for regular, ongoing feedback to let people know where they stand.

Good coaching is only one element of what you need to create a High Performing Team, but it is often the glue that links the vision with the outcomes.

The dictionary gives eight possible definitions for "coach." But the most important one is that of a tutor. A tutor isn't just a teacher, but someone who helps you build on the skills that you have already acquired. The definition that I prefer is a supportive relationship that fosters learning, transformation and growth. I think learning, transformation, and growth occur not only for the individual being coached but for the one doing the coaching as well. Each time we have the honor of helping someone else develop, we, too, are changed for the better.

To be successful, coaching requires a safe environment that helps individuals see themselves more clearly. Within that environment, the coaches need specific skills in order to be effective:

- The ability to acknowledge the other person's point of view
- The ability to challenge others when necessary
- Practicing active listening skills
- Being able to ask focused, thought-provoking questions
- The ability to ask for specific actions and behavior changes

The above list itemizes the skills that you need in coaching, but it is also important to understand the reasons *why* leaders need to be good coaches:

- To improve performance. In this case, it's assumed that the person you are coaching knows what to do and how to do it, but his performance may be inconsistent or sub-par.
- To correct problem behaviors. Coaching comes before disciplinary action. When you spot problem behaviors, coaching will help to bring the performance back in line with what is accept able.
- To encourage more good behavior. Coaching your high perform-

ers helps you to give them the challenges they need to remain engaged. At this level it is closely aligned with recognition as part of the coaching feedback cycle.

• To retain the brightest and best. People want to work for someone who helps them achieve their best and lets them know how they are doing.

Coaching is strong on direction and support. It assumes that you have done training but now are helping to move the person to the next level.

So why don't people coach when they should?

I find that there are four common reasons that leaders fail to engage in a coaching relationship. The first is that they lack confidence that they can be an effective coach. The second is that they lack coaching skills. The third, and perhaps the most prevalent, excuse is that leaders feel they lack the time to coach. But the fourth, and possibly the most dangerous excuse for not coaching, is that we think our team doesn't need it. Not so. Even the brightest and the best will get bored without a new challenge. Coaching helps the engaged employee stay that way.

When you commit to improving your own coaching skills, you will raise the bar in your department and your organization.

Coaching self-assessment:

Take an honest look at your skills. Ask others to give you feedback. Set goals for yourself. Share these goals with your boss and ask him to help you keep these goals in mind.

Coaching Self-Assessment			
	Rate your skill level 1 - 5 1= very poor 5= very strong	How would your staff rate you? 1 - 5 1= very poor 5= very strong	Identify areas for improvement
Setting expectations Coaches must set clear goals and expectations for performance.			
Observational skills Coaches must be able to observe performance and measure it against standards and goals.			
Analytical skills Coaches must be able to identify different learning styles in order to individualize coaching techniques.			
Active listening skills A coach must be able to listen respectfully and respond verbally and non-verbally. A coach must be able to engage staff in dialogue.			
Confronting skills Coaches must be able to confront individuals who are not meeting performance standards.			
Follow-through Coaches must be able to re-visit the issues and provide further feedback.			
Recognition & feedback Coaches must be able to recognize and reinforce positive changes.			
Communication Coaches must be able to communicate clearly and ask for commitment.			
Interest Coaches must have a genuine interest in helping others to achieve their goals.			
Support Coaches need to be able to provide an appropriate level of support without enabling negative or dependent behaviors.			

Based on your responses above, identify your priorities for improvement.

Work on your priorities by using the first three steps of the coaching process for your own growth.

1. Clarify what you want to achieve (goals and objectives).
2. Observe where you are now (baseline) and identify the gap between the baseline and your goal.
3. Specify action steps you need to take in order to close the gap.

Vince Lombardi said, "The dictionary is the only place where success comes before work." This applies not only to the people you are coaching but to you, the coach, as well. It may take some hard work in order to feel successful and confident in your coaching skills. Over the years, I have served as an executive coach for managers. I've created an acronym for them to use to remind them of five critical coaching steps:

C Clarify your goals and objectives.

O Observe the baseline as it relates to goals and objectives. Ask, "where are you now?"

A Actions to close the gap between baseline and goal.

C Communicate feedback that guides and encourages. Use active listening skills.

H Help them to identify and overcome barriers without enabling or coddling.

Example:

The housekeepers on your unit have a seven-point checklist for cleaning patient rooms. To improve the patient experience and cleanliness scores on the satisfaction survey, housekeepers were instructed to first introduce themselves upon entering a room and ask the patient's permission to clean it; and then to tell patients when they had finished cleaning the room and ask if the patient had any other needs.

The goal is to interact with the patients consistently during every cleaning encounter, in order to reinforce friendliness and a commitment to privacy. In addition, the housekeeper benefits from on-the-spot feedback in order to correct any cleaning problems.

During patient rounds, you learn that Michael, the day-shift housekeeper, is not introducing himself or asking the patient what else needs to be cleaned. When you make rounds you learn that in four out of 10 rooms (40 percent of the time), Michael has not talked with the patients. In order to manage Michael's performance, you prepare for the coaching encounter by reviewing how you will approach the problem using the five coaching steps.

Coaching encounter

Coaching step #1 - Clarify goal

Coach: Michael, when we talked about how we were going to improve our patient satisfaction scores related to room friendliness and cleanliness, we set two specific goals. Do you recall what the goals are?

Michael: Yes, we are supposed to introduce ourselves when we enter the room and then tell the patient when we have finished our cleaning checklist and ask if they see anything else that needs to be done.

Coach: That's right. The goal is to speak with the patient every time you clean a room.

Coaching Step #2 - Observe where he is now

Coach: The patients that you did speak with were impressed that you asked for their feedback. That's good, but your efforts need to be more consistent. I've noticed that you are talking with the patients sometimes, but not consistently. In fact, this week when I made my rounds, I found that you interacted with patients in four out of your 10 rooms.

Coaching Step #3 - Actions needed to close the gap between the goal and the current baseline

Coach: Michael, what can you do to make sure you are achieving the goals each time you clean a room?

Michael: I can put a reminder note on my cart. I can also take a moment to think about what I want to do before I go into the room.

Coach: Those sounds like good ideas, Michael. I will check back with you in a couple of days to see how that is working for you.

Coaching Step #4 - Communicate

Coach: I've noticed that you are improving. In fact, I have gotten good feedback from three of your patients today. How does this change feel to you?

Michael: It feels pretty good, but there are still times when I'm not following through. I'm still having some trouble.

Coaching Step #5- Help to identify and overcome barriers

Coach: Tell me about the times when you have had problems talking with the patients.
Michael: I'm still a bit uncomfortable interacting with the patient when they have visitors or if they are sleeping.

Coach: Well, I'm glad that you are sensitive to the patients' needs. That is really important. What might be some options for you?

Michael: I could come back to that room before I leave the unit and see if the patient is awake then. If they are still sleeping, I could leave a note with my pager number.

Coach: That is a great plan. I'll check back with you on Wednesday to find out how it is working for you.

Notice that in this scenario, the coach is giving Michael specific examples. The coach is not offering solutions, but is asking questions to evoke problem-solving on the part of the employee.

Problem-oriented coaching situations

One of the reasons for coaching is to correct problem behaviors. In this type of situation, you will want to clarify the results of the employee's behavior and the impact it is having. During the clarification step of the coaching process, use the XYZ formula when speaking with the employee.

The basis of this discussion boils down to this sentence: **"When you do X it causes Y. I would like you to do Z."** Then follow that statement with a request for their commitment. "Can I count on you to do that?" or, "Are you willing to do that?"

Example:

Your organization has a customer service standard aimed at creating a positive first impression. As part of that standard, employees are expected to make eye contact and greet all colleagues, patients, and visitors when passing them in the halls. You notice that Stephanie rarely greets visitors or patients and is selective about which colleagues she addresses. You decide to speak with her about her inconsistency in meeting the standard.

"Stephanie, when you walk past colleagues and visitors in the hall without speaking to them, you are giving an unfriendly, unwelcoming impression of our hospital. I would like you to consistently greet each person you pass in the halls. Can I count on you to do that?"

- **When you do X** - walk past colleagues and visitors in the hall without speaking to them,
- **It causes Y** - an unfriendly, unwelcoming impression of our hospital.
- **I would like you to do Z** - consistently greet each person you pass in the halls.
- **Ask for commitment** - Can I count on you to do that?

Don't forget the feedback. Let your staff know that you are noticing their improvements. Take the time to observe and give additional feedback. Try one or more of these statements: "It's obvious that you are really working on this." "Thanks." "How does this change feel to you?" "I appreciate your efforts."

Full-time role models

In his book, "Coaching For Improved Work Performance", Ferdinand F. Fournies talks about how the standard gets raised immediately when you acquire the title of manager. Fournies says, "You may have dozens of staff members, but your staff has only one boss. Each encounter with you, from their perspective, holds meaning."

Before becoming a manager or senior leader, you may have had the luxury of being able to have a bad day without much notice. But once you acquire a title that places you in the ranks of a leader, your actions are under scrutiny and open to interpretation.

Imagine having this type of day. You spilled your coffee into your lap. A newly posted detour made you 10 minutes late for a meeting you scheduled. You've got 20 things that need to be done by noon, and it's already 10 a.m. All you can think about is getting to your office, closing the door and getting focused on your tasks. You pass three of your staff on your way to your desk. You walk by Dave without saying a word. He thinks, "Uh-oh, she is still mad about my report being late last week." Then you pass by Michelle and again don't say a word, because your mind is focused on your task list. Michelle thinks, "Oh great, she has already heard about the debacle on nights, even though we worked everything out."

Just before you reach your office door, you get your game face back on and notice Maria coming down the hall. You look up, smile and say, "Good morning, Maria. It's great to see you." Maria thinks, "I love having such a personable leader."

Which employee is apt to feel more engaged? My point is, you don't get to excuse away your behavior with, "I'm only human" or "I'm having a bad day" when you are a leader. When you take on a leadership position and the accompanying title, you take on the duties of a full-time role model as well. People are watching, so you need to be more aware than ever of your behavior. If you expound the standards for service excellence, then walk past employees without speaking to them, you are sending a strong and memorable message.

How do you say "Welcome?"

Everyone knows you never get a second chance to make a good first impression, yet many human resource (HR) practices fall short when it comes to making job candidates feel welcome and enthusiastic about the organization. I'm not talking about how they are treated once inside the HR department; I'm talking about accessibility and response time. I have found very few HR departments accessible after 5 p.m. or on weekends. Think about it: If you are looking for a new job and still gainfully employed, what time are you available to interview? Online applications have helped make applying for jobs a 24/7 option, but how long does it take your HR department to respond to an online job inquiry? If you don't know the answer to that question, you should test the response by secret shopping your own services. You will want to find out:

- How long it takes to respond to a website inquiry
- How the department responds to phone inquiries
- Availability of after-hours interviews
- Once the interview is conducted, how long it takes for a candidate to get an offer

What steps do you take to ensure a good fit between the candidate and your organization?

A friend of mine works in an incredibly competitive market in California, where nurses are a precious commodity. During new employee orientation, she was having a casual conversation with a group of critical care nurses about how they made their decision to work with her organization. "That's easy," one of them told her. "You guys were the only ones who bothered to call me back. In fact, your HR people called me within two hours of my online application."

My friend went on to ask the nurses a few questions about their application process and response times from her hospital compared with those of competitors. It turns out that the nurses reported waiting one to two weeks for a response to an application, and others reported that their online and phone inquiries were never answered by the competitors at all.

While mystery shopping for my clients, I often show up in their HR departments to apply for jobs in order to provide them with some first-hand experiences. One hospital that stands out in my mind was engaged in a massive nurse recruitment campaign. I was really impressed with their brochures, table tents, and posters displayed throughout the campus. After spotting a 10- by 4-foot recruitment banner in the cafeteria, I decided to drop by HR to submit an application.

When I walked into the HR department, I was greeted by a friendly young woman. I told her that I wanted to apply for a nursing position and that I had experience in OB, critical care, med/surg and management. She asked if I had brought a resume with me. When I answered, "No, I was just visiting and saw your poster in the cafeteria," she told me, "I'm sorry. We don't really take applications here. But here is the card for our nurse recruiter. Call her and she can help you."

When I left the department, I had to check the sign on the door just to make sure that I had indeed walked into the HR department. No mistake. I had been in HR and was sent away to jump through the hoop of trying to reach the recruiter. My impression was that this organization wasn't as friendly or responsive as its flashy recruitment posters had led me to believe. When I left the department, I decided that I would be highly unlikely to pursue an application with this hospital. How many opportunities could you be losing? You'll never know unless you check it out.

This story is a classic example of how organizations can squander tens of thousands of dollars on recruitment campaigns, only to disappoint candidates at the point of contact. It is important for leaders to view the situation from the applicant's perspective in order to understand what kind of first impression the organization is giving potential job candidates.

Orientation

Orientation provides another great opportunity to engage employees in the values of the organization, yet so many organizations make new employee orientation sheer drudgery. Eight hours of people talking at you is neither engaging nor welcoming. Of course, each employer must complete the required JCAHO and OSHA requirements for patient and employee safety, but where's the fun? Where's the creativity? To engage adult learners, we need to make the subjects pertinent to them and help them understand how concepts apply to their positions and to their lives.

Take a good look at your orientation procedure and ask whose needs are being met in the way the orientation is designed. Is the format designed to accommodate the presenters and complete the "required" checklist, or is it designed to be interactive, engaging, and consistent with specified learning objectives?

A few years ago, I had an interesting encounter with an orientation committee whose members were holding fast to their ideas about how orientation should be managed. Everything was crammed into eight long, consecutive hours. Why? Because it worked best for the presenters and the managers who were "letting" their new employees attend.

It practically took an act of God to make this group consider any other alternatives than the way that they had always done things. But once they took a step back and created a new vision for orientation, they began to put pieces in place that created a much more positive first impression and worked wonders for engaging staff through an interactive process that was closely aligned with the orientation in the departments.

Telling stories is a great way to engage new hires in the culture of your organization. Tell stories of stellar service or of other new hires who went on to become some of your stellar performers. Use storytelling to teach the standards for service. Don't just read through the list of standards; tell stories of the standards in action, or, better yet, have some of your stellar performers tell stories about what service means and how they put the standards into action every day in their work.

Orientation is a great opportunity for you to lay the groundwork a new, and hopefully lasting, relationship. New employees are an incredibly valuable asset. In order for them to make contributions to your organization, they need first to be comfortable in their new environment, and that means getting settled in their new department and being given the tools that they need to do their jobs effectively.

If The Container Store® can devote 23 days to new employee orientation, why can't health care? I was in awe of The Container Store's onboarding process and was more than a little embarrassed that, although I have worked for several hospitals in the course of my 30-year career, I had never had the length and depth of orientation offered by this retail chain. It's no wonder that The Container Store ranks among our nation's great places to work.

All aboard!

Wikipedia defines onboarding as, "the process of interviewing, hiring, orienting and successfully integrating new hires into an organization's culture. The best onboarding strategies will provide a fast track to meaningful, productive work and strong employee relationships."

Organizations that embrace an onboarding system understand what it takes to help employees to feel welcome, engaged, valued and comfortable with their new surroundings.

In their book, "Customer Loyalty Guaranteed - Create, Lead and Sustain Remarkable Customer Service", authors Chip Bell and John Patterson compare new employee orientation to adoption: "Adopting a new family member involves a discussion of values, not just tasks; philosophy, not just benefits; customs, not just policies. In the business world, this adoption process serves as a powerful socialization tool that can bolster pride, ensure fit, and help new employees start to build important social networks."

Training and development

Learning infuses an organization with energy. When striving for a culture of service excellence, health care organizations need to introduce service behaviors early in the relationship with any new employee. Then, the behaviors must be reinforced regularly, and consistently linked back to the mission, vision, strategy, and brand.

Knowledge-transfer occurs when newly acquired skills are reinforced within the department. If an employee learns about the service philosophy in orientation but then sees something completely different once on the unit, he or she will become disillusioned and disconnected quickly. That type of disconnect can destroy corporate credibility in a heartbeat.

One way to avoid this type of disconnect is to create comprehensive, organization-wide orientation practices whose objectives bridge house-wide orientation curriculum to the departments' orientation objectives. Make sure managers know what is covered in the orientation curriculum and are prepared to reinforce that information on the unit.

Ongoing development helps keep staff engaged. Liberty Lutheran in Philadelphia does a great job of this in their Core Competency Training program. After a comprehensive orientation, their staff attends training at least one hour per month to continually reinforce values and standards. Their approach is to make their priorities very clear during hiring and orientation, and then to reinforce them continually through ongoing development.

It is important for leaders to take an honest look at how we treat orientation and staff development. I shudder to think what our educational system would be like if school districts approached education like we do our orientation and training in many health care organizations. In classrooms, teachers assess new students' baseline knowledge and have continual learning objectives throughout the school year. All lessons roll up to fit within the objectives.

I have worked with many organizations that treat orientation as a necessary evil on their "to do" list. Subsequent staff development occurs haphazardly, at best, and without much in the way of a master plan.

Leaders who are serious about creating and sustaining a culture of excellence must make certain that new employee orientation and ongoing staff development efforts consistently mesh with organizational priorities.

Action steps:

- Review the new employee orientation curriculum and draw correlations between the organizational priorities and the orientation content.
- Evaluate the onboarding process to determine how new employees are supported, welcomed, and integrated into the culture. How are key messages delivered in orientation and reinforced once the employee is on the unit?

Listen and act!

What are your employees telling you about the culture and the people in it?

Listening to your employees is an absolute must in fostering a culture of excellence. If you haven't been measuring employee satisfaction, it's time to start. Earlier in this chapter, I cited studies that validate the correlation between employee satisfaction and patient satisfaction. But measuring won't fix the problem; it only helps to identify the symptoms.

My colleagues and I have worked with a number of organizations that still cringe when we ask about how and how often they measure employee satisfaction. It astounds me that in this day and age, we still encounter leaders who tell us that they aren't measuring regularly, because they still haven't done anything about the last set of scores! You can rationalize all you want, but this mindset is the old "ignore it and hope it goes away" approach. If you are guilty of this, ask yourself how well this is working for you. What results are you seeing? If you are like the other leaders I have spoken with, your results are nil.

I am always amused when the same leaders who take this "ignore it and hope it goes away" approach with employee satisfaction are adamant about action plans and timelines for improving patient satisfaction. The two go hand-in-hand. A culture of excellence must strive for the best in employee satisfaction and physician satisfaction, as well as patient satisfaction. You won't have one without the others.

When you measure employee satisfaction, use the information to create a tangible action plan for improvement. Engage others in creating the plan and communicate it widely. Let your employees know what problems have been identified, and ask for their involvement. If there are opportunities to serve on action teams, invite staff to sign up. By involving them, they become owners of the solutions and will give your efforts a jump-start.

Talk it up!

During employee focus groups, participating staff members often tell us that they don't give much credibility to employee satisfaction surveys. "Nothing ever happens with the information," they say. "Nothing ever changes, so why should I participate? We tell them the same thing year after year." In some organizations that may be true. But often, the leaders are creating action plans behind closed doors and not sharing the plans or involving others in formulating plans.

One of the biggest mistakes leaders make is to conduct employee satisfaction surveys and then keep the results and the action plan under wraps. Tell the entire staff that you've identified priorities and that you will form action teams to address the priorities.

If you spend the time and money to hear what your employees are thinking, you owe it to yourself and to them to use the information to make improvements. But, like it or not, your employees won't instinctively know that you are taking action based on that information; you have to tell them what is going on. At the organizational level, share the overall findings and identify the priorities that have been set for making improvements. At the department level, review department scores as well as organizational scores, solicit additional feedback and enlist support for making necessary improvements. One of the best ways to present this information is a team approach, including a representative from senior leadership and the department manager. That way, staff can see that the information is being shared openly, without blame or retribution, but rather to elicit solutions and involvement.

Above all, communication is the key to helping staff to feel that they have been heard and that action is being taken. You cannot over-communicate with your employees. It is better to let them know the action plans and the players involved in implementing the plan than to just assume that they know you are taking action.

Post updates that describe the various teams, their goals, members and progress toward the goals. Continually recognize the teams for their achievements.

When communicating about the survey findings and action plans, there are three messages or action steps that should be stated:

- Review how information was shared from your most recent employee satisfaction survey.
- Get feedback from staff about how they feel the information was handled.
  - * Were scores shared openly?
  - * Did managers and senior leaders inform them of action steps being taken to make improvements?
  - * Were staff given the opportunity to join teams or give input for how to make improvements?
- Commit to engaging employees in action teams.
- Commit to communicating survey results and action plans resulting from the information.

Raise the bar by expecting the best

Great leaders have high expectations for themselves as well as for their constituents. Communicating that you believe in your staff and in their ability to exceed in customer service is vital to your success. The Pygmalion effect has been demonstrated in a number of situations in and outside of business. Leaders who raise the bar, setting high expectations, while communicating their faith that the staff can rise to the challenge, more often than not will get the desired results.

Customize your approach for maximum results

Parenting taught me several valuable lessons in leadership. My three daughters are all very different people and, although I was clear about my standards and expectations in my home, my approach to dealing with each of my three children was unique and tailored to each daughter's individual strengths and personality. In order to help each of them to maximize her potential, I had to understand what made her tick. In "Customer Loyalty Guaranteed", Bell and Patterson identify what they call "loyalty creators." These are seven different service styles, characterized by unique strengths. The authors classify the service styles as Joy Carrier, Partner, Caretaker, Problem Solver, Decorator, Conscience, and Giver. They not only clarify the strengths inherent in each style, they discuss how to most effectively engage and lead that type of individual.

For instance, the authors describe how the Problem Solver digs into customer complaints until he or she finds a solution: "The Problem Solver's need to repair what is broken is a vital part of who he is - almost compulsively so at times. The Problem Solver needs a leader who can help him focus his efforts, as he can quickly become myopic in his quest to unsnarl details. Good leaders prompt the Problem Solver to keep his eye on the long view and not be seduced by a quick fix."

Similarly, the Joy Carrier is enthusiastic about life in general and brings that vibrant energy to work. In many cases, the Joy Carriers' gifts help draw people to them. But in other situations, Joy Carriers can overwhelm people with their exuberance. A good leader will help the Joy Carriers to learn to read others around them so they can temper their exuberance so as not to overwhelm or turn people off.

It's important for leaders to take inventory of staff and recognize their unique gifts. Leaders will form stronger relationships with team members when they can clearly see each person's unique gifts and then work with them to make the best possible use of those gifts. In doing so, you will be leveraging one of your greatest assets in building customer loyalty.

Physicians

In order to maximize your people power, don't overlook the medical staff. They are essential in creating a culture of excellence. In order to achieve measurable and sustainable service results, the physicians must be involved and demonstrate leadership and commitment to the cause.

We are often asked when to get the medical staff involved in service. The timing is important. If you try to tackle the medical staff from the beginning of your culture-shifting process, you may have difficulty. My advice is to communicate with physicians in the very early stages of your culture-enhancing initiative. Let them know that you are committed to excellence and talk about the steps you are taking to make measurable improvements. Remind them that there are compelling reasons to commit to service excellence - not the least of which is physician satisfaction, as well as employee and patient satisfaction. Keep them apprised of changes and improvements as they occur. Once you can demonstrate that the rest of the organization is on board and making progress, you will have more leverage in encouraging physician involvement. In many cases, when physicians see that scores are increasing, they become believers in the process and want to get involved.

But don't be surprised by, or shy away from, resistance from physicians. It can be difficult to get physicians on board with a service initiative. Staying the course and not wavering in your quest for service excellence will send a clear message that a culture of customer service is here to stay.

Every organization I have worked with wants to know the secret to getting physicians engaged in service. Encouraging physician buy-in is no different with customer service than with any other goal. One of the secrets to engaging physicians is having an open and trusting relationship. Does the leadership do what they promise? Is follow-up consistent? Are the physicians treated with respect?

Getting physicians engaged in customer service is simply an extension of their existing relationship with the organization. As with the link between employee satisfaction and patient satisfaction, your physicians' investment in service will only be as strong as their relationship with you.

Don't assume that the physicians understand why service excellence is so important. Make sure that they understand why you are involved in service improvement. If you talk only about market share and the bottom line, you are very likely to lose them in the process. Communicate consistently that the primary reason for service excellence is to create a place where patients want to come for care, where physicians want to practice and where employees want to work. In his book, "Practice Excellence - A Physician's Manual to Exceptional Health Care", Stephen C. Beeson, MD, identifies five cases for improved service. He cites well-documented evidence that a service-centered culture will:

- Enhance patient compliance
- Promote growth, market share and loyalty
- Reduce malpractice risk
- Improve physician/staff relationship
- Strengthen physician relationships with colleagues

Beeson states, "The literature is so overwhelming in terms of the impact of service and communication on clinical outcomes, malpractice risk, loyalty, growth, patient satisfaction, and organizational success, that this really is no longer up for debate. ... Medical groups simply cannot compete in this current medical marketplace without engaging the tools that work to drive the patient experience."

Having a physician champion will help you to gain traction much more quickly. The champion needs to be well respected among the medical staff and have a good rapport with senior leaders and staff as well. The champion will help the medical staff to develop a vision and standards for service excellence. Beeson calls this person the Physician Fire Starter and offers information on how to select train, and support the Physician Fire Starter.

Data, data everywhere - and not a drop of information!

Is your patient satisfaction data providing physicians with useful information? An article in HealthLeaders Magazine (Fact File, July 1, 2007) cited research showing that 46 percent of physicians surveyed said that patient satisfaction data was rarely or never used to change patient care. I have to wonder if that is because the physicians don't understand the data or how they pertain to the actual patient encounter.

In order to continue raising the bar on service excellence, physicians need to know what the surveys are asking. I have talked with a number of physicians who have told me they have no idea what their patient satisfaction scores mean or how to go about improving them. They feel pressured to improve, but don't see the link between the scores and how their behavior influences the patient experience in their day-to-day encounters.

I was recently asked to do mystery shopping on physicians who were among the lowest scoring in their practice. As part of this particular mystery shop, I was also engaged to follow up with the physicians to give them the first-hand report of my assessment and do some one-on-one coaching with each of them. When I was talking with one of the physicians, I showed him the criteria I used and talked him through exactly why I scored him the way I did. He was surprised to learn that one of the survey questions meant something totally different from what he'd thought.

If the physicians don't understand how they are being judged, they won't be able to formulate a targeted action plan for improvement. Don't leave this up to chance.

Action steps:

- Distribute patient satisfaction survey to physicians.
- Ask them to take the survey as though they were scoring themselves through the patients' eyes.

- Conduct small group sessions where physicians can compare how they scored themselves with how the patients actually scored them.
- Provide them with best practices and action planning tools.

Raising the Bar:
Parkview engages physicians in service excellence

Like many organizations committed to improving service, Parkview Medical Center (PMC) in Pueblo, Colorado, grappled with how to get physicians engaged and more accountable. Elliott Ring, PMC's director of organizational effectiveness, helped to set the standards for service behaviors for all employees and led the initiative to get staff training and involved in living the standards. Although PMC was making headway on patient satisfaction scores, they weren't seeing much progress in the ED. That's when Ring began collaborating with Dr. Shawn Gogarty and Dr. Thomas G. Greidanus to get the physicians more engaged in performance improvement.

Greidanus had just taken over from Gogarty the positions of medical director, ddepartment chair, and president of Southern Colorado Emergency Medical Associates, the emergency physician group under contract with PMC. Greidanus as well as the other ED physicians knew the benefits of a long term contract with PMC, so when the pressure to improve patient satisfaction scores started to mount, Greidanus and Gogarty knew they had to find a way to get their physicians focused on making positive changes.

"When we first got our department's patient satisfaction scores, the physicians pointed fingers and placed blame because all of the physicians were lumped together in one report," explains Greidanus. "It was always the other guy, not me, who was dragging down the scores."

So Ring and Greidanus worked with Avatar International, Inc., their survey vendor, to separate out the data by individual provider.

"Once the data was filtered, each provider could see his or her own scores, which helped make the information more believable," says Greidanus. "Of course, we still had some naysayers, but at least the data was specific."

In order to put teeth into their expectations of the medical staff, Greidanus negotiated with the hospital to provide a bonus for individual physicians based on their patient satisfaction scores. Knowing that you can't change behavior with financial incentives alone, Greidanus implemented a quarterly feedback system and concentrated on public praise for high performers and private critiques for those not performing up to par.

Ring helped to coach low performers on specific behaviors that would help to improve patient satisfaction. In addition, he sought out feedback from the nurses. The nurses were asked to gauge physician interactions with patients, and to make suggestions for how the physician could improve. "The nurses' feedback was extremely helpful in communicating with the physicians," says Ring. "The nurses' feedback helped me to approach the physicians with an appreciative inquiry style. I could start each conversation with a discussion of their strengths, rather than hitting them over the head with what they need to improve," says Ring. "With the nurses' feedback in combination with the patient feedback, the physicians started to listen. Many of them started to realize that their satisfaction scores had more to do with what and how they communicate. Once they started to pay attention to their communication styles, they started to make huge improvements."

At one time, physician Chad Davis ranked consistently low on the satisfaction surveys, but was insightful enough to listen to the nurses' review. Now Davis consistently places in the top three or four in the physician group and is ranked high within the peer group as well. He has become a role model for other physicians and helps mentor them in making improvements.

"We tell the doctors who are still struggling with satisfaction to take a look at the physicians who rank in our top three and follow them around and find out what makes them successful," says

Greidanus. "It is amazing how something as simple as pulling up a stool to be at the patient's eye level can make a huge difference in the patient experience. We also promote scripting and empathetic talk as important elements of communication."

"In order to get the physicians to work on their skills, we looked at some best practices and brainstormed about how we could implement some of the best strategies. We made it mandatory for the physicians to participate in service improvement and just kept pushing it along," says Greidanus.

Greidanus and Ring are pleased to see a statistically significant increase in their scores rising from the low-to high-80s. Both admit that the journey hasn't been easy. "I have had several older doctors tell me that this is all a bunch of crap," says Greidanus. "At one point I had to tell a physician, 'Just stop arguing over the statistics and start improving your performance.' I know that if that message would have been sent by the CEO, it wouldn't have worked, but the physicians know that I rank very high in our peer group, so I am living it each shift like they do."

When asked what he would recommend to other medical groups that want to make improvements, Greidanus said, "Persistence and not letting the doctors get out of it. Send a message that this is important and it is not going away."

A case for caring

Although there are numerous journal articles about the measurable results of customer service, my own experiences are also conclusive. Research shows that compliance improves when physicians foster a respectful, caring relationship with patients. The data speaks for itself, but my own experience further reinforces it.

One example involved my sister, Patty, who is mentally retarded, yet a remarkably determined woman. Patty has done exceptionally well with minimal guidance. In the past few years, she has developed medical problems and has needed regular visits to the doctor.

When getting ready for one of her visits, I was reviewing her medication list with her to verify that she was indeed taking all of her medications as prescribed. I praised her for remembering to take her asthma inhaler regularly. She said, "Well, I have to. My doctor really cares about me. He told me that he worries about my asthma and that I need to take my inhaler. I like him. I don't want him to worry about me, so I do what he says." As simplistic as this example may seem, it sums up the value of fostering a trusting relationship. It just doesn't get any clearer than that. Patty wants to comply with her doctor's orders because her doctor let her know how much he cares about her and that he is concerned about her well-being.

As for reducing malpractice risk, this one seems fairly obvious. Simply stated, people don't often sue people they like. Again, rather than cite a plethora of journal articles, I'd rather share what I know from personal experience.

About four years ago a friend of mine underwent a major surgery for cancer. If her diagnosis wasn't bad enough, the treatment became as life-threatening as the disease when her surgeon left a 13-inch retractor in her abdomen.

She lived with excruciating pain for over three weeks, and the mistake ended up causing a severe infection and a punctured lung. When I talked with her immediately after the discovery, I was astounded when she told me that she had no plans to sue her physician. She told me, "I really love her and respect her. I would never do anything to harm her career. She has been so good to me."

In our litigious society, it is almost expected that people sue for such mistakes. It was refreshing to hear her voice her loyalty. Unfortunately, she did pursue a lawsuit against the hospital and, ultimately, the physician was brought into it as well. But the real message is that she was loyal to her physician because of a trusting relationship.

A few last thoughts about the power of people

At the risk of sounding cliché, your people are your greatest asset. That begs the question: Are you taking specific actions to raise the bar to make the most of this asset, or are you merely paying lip service? When you understand the elements that cause someone to want to join and stay with your organization, you will have some of the most important knowledge necessary for building and sustaining the work force you need to fulfill your mission and vision in line with your priorities. When you take actions to hire right, engage, and develop continuously, you will have a powerhouse of potential at your fingertips.

Leader reflections

Reflect and journal on the following:

- What are your beliefs about the link between employee engagement and patient satisfaction?
- How do your organizational priorities align with hiring, orienting, and developing your people?
- What are three things that you do consistently to model service excellence?
- What stands in the way of having a fully engaged work force?
- What messages are you sending that demonstrate your faith in your team?
- What is the relationship like between the medical staff and senior leaders? Is it trusting, respectful, and collaborative?

Actions

- Create a compelling vision for your work force.
- Engage senior leaders in reviewing the hiring and onboarding activities in context of your organizational priorities.
- Identify gaps and create an action plan to close the existing gaps.
- Review how you have communicated past employee satisfaction results. Solicit employee feedback about how your methods helped them to understand goals and action steps.
- Consider findings from all previous action steps in creating a

robust curriculum for leadership training that includes:
* Employee engagement strategies and tactics
* Coaching for improved performance
* Onboarding strategies for improved retention and engage-
    ment

Chapter Three

"It's the little things that make the big things possible. Only close attention to the fine details of any operation makes the operation first class."

- J. Willard Marriott

You've set clear priorities, and you've put the right people in place to work toward achieving them. Now, it's time to make sure your team has the processes in place to support them in their task.

Take a good look at how your team functions right now. It's helpful to conduct a process audit to discover what's working - and what's not - in the way your organization provides services today. Ask yourself: Do you have good customer service processes in place? Are the processes efficient? Do the processes support staff in delivering excellent, customer-related services? Do staff members at all levels of the organization have the opportunity to offer input for business improvement? Are they encouraged to be innovative in improving systems and processes?

You'll need to know the answers to these questions, and more, as you evaluate your organization's service performance.

An organization's leaders may not be the people who will actually define or reconfigure processes. That task goes to another team. But leaders can and should promote a culture that encourages and rewards efficiency, quality and service - all of which are closely linked to processes.

Recently, I had dinner with a friend who had once owned a restaurant franchise based in the Midwest. As we prepared the meal, I noticed how methodically she prepared the lettuce for our salads. Did she have a touch of obsessive-compulsive disorder, I wondered? Or did she know something about lettuce that I didn't?

When I asked her why she made a precision V-cut on each leaf of romaine lettuce, she laughed. "It's a force of habit now," she said. "(At the franchise) we had a procedure in place for everything, and were expected to follow them without exception. This is the process we used to prep the lettuce for the day's salads."

She went on to describe the preparation involved in becoming the owner of a restaurant franchise. First, potential owners spend months in training as store managers to learn the official ways of the franchise; then, they spend several more months at other stores, observing the practices of seasoned managers. All of these obligations have to be met before an owner can open his own store. "They are very particular about making sure that customers get the same quality food at each of their restaurants," she explained. "They're very protective of the franchise operation."

Her description of the restaurant franchise process left me dumbfounded - and a bit embarrassed. By comparison, in health care - where our customers are placing their very lives in our hands - new employees typically have a one- or two-day orientation before they're rushed to a unit. Of course, clinical competency is expected based on prior training, certification, and licensure. I'm referring specifically to how we "on-board" new employees and immerse them into the culture. It seems that little, if any, time is spent immersing new employees in the organization's "way of doing things." And I've even seen managers postpone or shorten a new employee's orientation. Why? Health care organizations are short-staffed, and employees (read: warm bodies) are needed on the units as soon as possible.

How is it that a restaurant chain can hold its franchises accountable for specific food-handling procedures, but the health care business leaves so much about the patient experience up to chance? Of course, we do have policies and procedures to safeguard clinical practices, particularly those related to patient and staff safety. But I have never seen an orientation process for a health care employee as comprehensive as the one described by this restaurant franchise owner.

What if your health care organization were to run customer service functions with the same consistency that this restaurant franchise expects from its owners? What standards would you set? How would you familiarize new employees with the way things are done in your hospital or your department? And at what point would you feel confident that a new hire was ready to go forward and work on his own?

If your culture is "they way we do things around here," then every process that you put into place is a reflection of the culture. The culture, in turn, is a direct reflection of the processes that are put into place. Processes and culture are a cyclic dynamic. This is not to say that every process is carefully thought out or prescribed through a policy and procedure manual. In fact, it is many of the undocumented processes that drive the culture and attitudes. If you want to create a customer-centric culture, you must ensure that the systems and processes you put into place support the desired culture. I t must happen by design, not by default.

Leading a culture that's committed to excellence demands rigorous attention to processes. But if our processes don't support our top priorities, we'll be sending mixed messages to the staff, and breeding confusion and discontent. Reliable processes don't lead to robotic employees; rather, they form a foundation that provides a reliable structure for safety, quality, service, and innovation. Processes becomes habit, and habits create comfortable routines that, in turn, create more consistency in the customer experience.

The terms "quality improvement" and "process" go hand-in-hand. This pairing has long been embraced in health care, as evidenced by voluminous procedure manuals that support our commitment to processes in the clinical area. Nevertheless, when we think about fostering service and innovation, we often lack the very structure and processes that we associate with clinical successes.

Some processes can be condensed down to a checklist, which may be the simplest form of process management. Writers Dan Heath and Chip Heath laud the benefits of the checklist in their article, "The Heroic Checklist - Why You Should Learn to Love Checking Boxes", in the March 2008 issue of Fast Company magazine. "How can something so simple be so powerful?" they ask. "Checklists are good because they can educate people about the best course of action, showing them the ironclad right way to do something."

The writers cite an example of how a simple five-point checklist significantly decreased intravenous infections in patients of the intensive care unit (ICU). The creator of the checklist, Dr. Peter Pronovist of the Johns Hopkins University School of Medicine, had realized that infections related to the intravenous lines were preventable. By condensing crucial actions down to a prescribed checklist, Pronovist hoped to reduce the number and severity of related infections.

The checklist, according to the article, contained straightforward advice: "Doctors should wash their hands before inserting an IV, a patient's skin should be cleaned with an antiseptic at the point of insertion," and so forth. There was no new science and nothing controversial - only the results were surprising. When Michigan ICUs put the checklist into practice over a period of 18 months, line infections were virtually eliminated, saving the hospitals an estimated $175 million, because they no longer had to treat the associated complications. In addition, they go on to write, this simple process was credited with saving about 1,500 lives.

So, which areas need to have specific processes in place? Just the ones you want to be successful. In other words, plan for your success. It's not enough to say, "Just do it." As a leader, you must make sure that your staff has all the tools it needs to raise that bar.

The University of Utah Hospitals and Clinics is an excellent example of an organization that has improved processes to optimize the patient experience. Robin Lloyd is the executive director for ambulatory services and ccommunity clinics for the system. In 2003, Lloyd and his team made an unyielding commitment to improve the patient experience in their 10 community clinics, which span four counties.

Raising the bar:
Utah clinics' processes focus on patients

A plan to open a new community clinic was the impetus for change in The University of Utah Hospitals and Clinics (UUHC). Wanting to be more patient-focused, efficient, and cost effective, Community Clinics (CC) leaders saw that they had a unique opportunity to revamp how they had done things in the past.

When drilling down into many existing processes, I often find that a large percent of processes and systems are designed in the physician's best interest, not the patient's. Like many organizations, CC found this to be the case with many of their established processes.

To shift the focus from provider-centered to patient-centered, CC leaders did research with area consumers. Their research showed that patients wanted three things: efficiency in service, the ability to participate in their own care during their visits, and printed summaries of their appointments. The research also revealed that patients didn't want excessive waiting times, multiple moves, and having to repeat information over and over again.

Armed with the new information about patient likes and dislikes, the CC team set out to analyze the clinics' existing processes, mapping out entire patient encounters using lean design principles that eliminate waste and improve efficiencies in systems. The team found that in some cases, as much as three-fourths of the process was wasted time and of no value to the patient. Entirely new processes had to be designed to support patients' needs.

Process change came about through the work of a multidisciplinary team of functional directors from the quality, clinical and IT areas. The team was charged with redesigning clinic operations. Lloyd credits his team with innovative process change. "We have talented people who came together to redesign the patient flow and the building itself," Lloyd recalls. "We looked for best practices and began planning the processes based on what we had learned. In some areas there were no best practices, so we had to design our own. But we never wavered from our mission to keep the systems and processes patient-centered."

The team applied six principles to the task:

1. Focus on the patient experience. This experience starts with the call center and pre-registration. Because patients didn't want to have to move around a lot and switch from provider to provider, the team created a new process where the patient would be accompanied throughout their visits and would receive an after-visit summary.

2. Right person, right job. Using micro practices as their model, CC leaders reorganized staff into care teams. One significant change was in redesigning the medical assistant (MA) function. Added responsibilities and cross training raised the medical assistant position into a higher pay grade. The MAs were required to do things differently and, in the process, totally redefined provider flow and built micro system teams. The practice also began to tap into the support of off-site services.

3. Standardization. The CC team sought to build systems and practices that would be standard in all the organization's clinics. For example, the same electrionic medical record (EMR) is now used at every site. In addition, they identified several "small" things that were big time wasters. One such example was placing a printer in every room to save providers from having to run down the hall to retrieve documents. This simple change saved significant staff time. Exam rooms were standardized in design, layout and supplies. Ordering protocols and scheduling were all standardized as well.

In many medical practices, only one person knows a physician's preferences and work habits. That can be a problem when that one person gets sick or goes on vacation. The CC team promoted standardization of the physician work styles to avoid such problems. That change required that teams of three or four people be cross-trained and coached to become familiar with the way the physicians liked things done. Many of the physicians' activities were standardized with smart techs and smart forms.

4. Facilities. The team designed a plan to accommodate the patients' needs and the staff's workflow for the most positive experience and the greatest efficiency. That included having exam rooms flanking two sides of a central corridor that houses supplies and allows providers to move efficiently between exam rooms.

5. Exploit technology. The team found several examples of how small things made a huge difference. The EMR was one use of technology. The staff went wireless, and used pagers and cordless phones with earpieces to communicate with one another. An off-site call center was used for scheduling and a pharmacy protocol and diabetic registry were created, all using modern technologies.

6. Communication: For smooth, efficient, and comprehensive communication, the organization implemented stand-up staff meetings, hung bulletin boards, and had "team huddles" between the doctors and the care team members. They also added radios and headsets for staff to be able to communicate with one another, without pulling them away from their patients.

The real measure of success is that the new practice has reduced the patient cycle time from two hours to 45 minutes, and patient satisfaction has increased by 30 percentile points. In addition, turnover among the MAs has decreased significantly. Lloyd attributes the reduction in turnover to the staff having greater challenges, which allows them to hone new skills. With greater efficiencies, staff lives are better. In addition to the efficiencies, staff reports fewer interruptions and complaints from unhappy patients, both of which contribute to greater employee satisfaction.

Many organizations shy away from process change, because it is difficult to get physician support. Building physician buy-in for process change can pose problems. Habits are habits, and we all have a tendency to believe that the way we do things is the best way. So it didn't come as a surprise that physicians had some difficulty early in the CC transition. "But once they tried it and saw that these processes worked, they were much more likely to buy in," says Lloyd.

Plus, when patients express greater satisfaction, the medical staff is much more likely to buy into the changes. Today, the CC physicians report that they can accomplish more in the same period of time, all because their work functions have been reorganized.

Early in the redesign process, a visiting physician spoke with the doctors about the importance of redesigning processes. When he told them that their time is worth $6 a minute he got the physician's attention. They could see that if they had to run down the hall to get the MA, or pull lab results off the printer in another room, it's not only expensive, it's exhausting. That message resonated with the medical staff, because they could see the value of more efficient processes. Electronic scheduling, putting printers in each exam room, standardized exam room setup, and changing the MA's role made a huge difference to the CC doctors.

The CC team wove a quality thread through all the new process changes. The process improvements have made an impact on the diabetes initiative, colon cancer screening, and preventative care. For the CC, quality and process improvement are ongoing endeavors. The team is now working with the college of business to organize its new model into an analytical design. Their goal is to continue quantifying process and outcomes.

The successes at the University of Utah Community Clinics demonstrate the leadership and teamwork required in processes improvement. Without collaboration and a clear vision among the leaders, the positive changes wouldn't have been possible; at the first inkling of resistance or discomfort, the efforts would have ceased. Instead, by focusing on the mission of the organization and needs of the patients, Lloyd and his team have designed and implemented a best practice.

Apply processes for efficiency and quality

This chapter provides examples of how to build processes that help build continuity and momentum among staff, and support customer service. I've also outlined examples of essentials for innovation, experience mapping, and service recovery. There are so many examples, I could have provided a list extensive enough to warrant a separate publication - but for the sake of simplicity, I've limited them to topics related to some of our most frequently asked questions.

Process for the customer service team

One way you can ensure more consistent progress toward improved patient and employee satisfaction is by having a clear framework for your customer service team. Once this framework is in place, the team can create specific processes to foster a culture of excellence. To be successful, the Service Excellence Team (SET) needs a strong champion who won't lose sight of priorities or leave crucial tasks undone.

Select the customer service champion

The success of your team - and of the entire service initiative - is directly linked to the performance of the customer service champion, so it is vital that you select the best person for the job. The champion must be passionate about service, and she must have credibility and influence at all levels of your organization; ideally, she'll be at the senior level.

Some organizations are now recognizing the value of having a chief experience officer who makes customer service his No. 1 focus. But be cautious; make sure that all senior leaders, directors, managers and supervisors understand that while the title or responsibility has been assigned to a particular person, they must still take ownership and responsibility for service in their own departments. The champion leads the effort, but the other leaders must actively support her by holding their departments accountable for results.

Without a united front from senior leaders, the champion is out on the battlefield alone - unarmed and without backup. She shouldn't have to fight this cause alone. So, if your senior leaders aren't prepared to stand together in a quest for excellence, put this book down and focus your attention elsewhere. You won't be able to achieve sustainable change without commitment from the entire senior leadership team.

In Chapter Two (People), I identified the connection between the responsibilities of customer service staff and the responsibilities of various other job roles. It should now be clear that the responsibility for fostering a culture of excellence lies with all leaders in an organization, regardless of rank.

My colleagues and I have worked with many organizations that have put the responsibility for an entire service initiative on one person who is a supervisor or coordinator, rather than a member of senior leadership. Often, this person is the one who has gathered and reported survey results. So, on the surface, it seems logical to put him in charge of customer service.

However, we've found, positive changes happen slowly - if at all - in most of these situations, and the individual in charge winds up frustrated and burned out. Here's the problem: Someone at a coordinator or supervisory level may well have the passion to take on the task, and the ability to understand the satisfaction scores. But without leadership clout, he won't have the influence to move the mountains that can stand in the way of true accountability. He has responsibility, but no authority. Although the end results depend on the culture of the organization, we've found that generally, a service champion's efforts are ignored or discounted by directors, managers, staff and physicians if he doesn't have leadership status.

In order to be effective, your customer service champion should have:

Authority - In order to shift the culture, the champion will have to challenge the status quo. Therefore, having legitimate authority within the organization will give her the edge.

Leadership ability - Title alone does not create leaders. Identify someone others want to follow. Who can communicate a compelling vision and engage others in a common cause?

Persistence - Change doesn't happen overnight. The leader must be prepared to persevere in the face of adversity.

Facilitation skills -The champion must be able to harness creative talents of all the team members, and keep them moving toward clearly defined goals, without micromanaging.

Organizational skills - Shifting culture requires many moving parts. The champion needs to keep tabs on a number of activities and metrics related to service. Good organizational skills will help him manage to juggle various responsibilities.

Enthusiasm - Infectious enthusiasm is crucial. Energy can wane over time, particularly if results are slow. An optimistic champion sees progress and continually encourages others.

A winning team model

Throughout my years as both an administrator and consultant, I have worked with and refined the Baird Model, a process that helps provide structure to the customer service initiative:

If you have processes in place, your customer service team can have clearer objectives and move toward them more efficiently. Many well-meaning customer service teams have met for years and have yet to achieve measurable results. Why? They're going in too many directions; they have no clearly defined goals.

The five-pointed star of the Baird Model has proven useful in organizing customer service teams. When you draw a five-pointed star, you can begin at any point and you will eventually intersect with all the other points. Because the five elements - innovation, communication, measurement, recognition, and standards - are all vital to the success of a team or organization, we chose the star as our symbol, because it is simple and memorable.

A customer service team needs direction and clarity of purpose. Members need to stay unified and on task. To achieve this, you can organize your team around these five primary objectives:

- To create clear, observable, behavior-based standards for service excellence, and to integrate them into hiring processes, training objectives, and performance appraisals
- To link standards to recognition and performance evaluations in order to support accountability; to promote recognition in peer relationships, department operations and across the organization
- To have clear, measurable goals; the ability to quantify patient satisfaction and employee engagement; and, ultimately, the ability to turn that data into action with measurable results
- To structure communication strategies and tactics that deliver consistently clear messages about the link between organizational mission, vision and values and customer service activities
- To foster innovation that engages staff in supporting the strategic plan and rewards creative problem solving

When we work with customer service teams, we help them to mobilize specific task forces under each of these five objectives. But in order to be successful, these teams need to remain unified in their vision and direction. The five teams are given specific charges:

1. Standards team

If your organization has already established customer service standards, the standards team is responsible for ensuring that these standards are communicated to staff on a regular basis. The team must also make sure that these standards are clearly linked to recognition and accountability. In addition to providing education, the standards team will work closely with human resources to incorporate the standards into hiring practices, job descriptions, and performance appraisals. Processes will need to be in place to:

- expose job candidates to the standards during the initial interview
- gain commitment to standards at the time of the job offer
- train new employees on the service standards during initial orientation
- incorporate standards into job descriptions
- incorporate standards into performance appraisals
- tie standards to recognition and communication
- help department managers to reinforce standards in daily operations
- create ongoing education on the standards

Once these processes are in place, it is up to the department leaders to manage them and hold people accountable.

2. Measurement team

Simply stated, the function of the measurement team is to turn data into action. It must make sure that the satisfaction data is not only widely distributed, but is also used in forming specific action teams. We call these teams SWAT (Strategies, Work plans, Actions and Tactics) teams. The measurement task force creates processes to make sure that SWA T teams are formed, and that plans are executed in each department with measurable goals and specific action plans. This function has a direct connection to innovation, because successful teams create innovative solutions to problems.

This is, by far, one of the most important functions of the SET. It can also be very challenging. After all, if you are measuring patient satisfaction, you need to act on what you discover. You're asking patients to give you honest feedback about their experiences with you; the very least you can do in return is to commit to listening to what they say and to using their feedback to initiate changes.

I have found that organizations that keep the data close to the front line staff are the most effective at fostering change. If it takes you months to get data to your employees, you're missing key opportunities to engage staff in making necessary changes. Staff can't fix something that they don't know about, so a key function of the measurement team is to make sure the data reaches the front line staff in a timely manner, so problem solving can begin.

Departments that appoint one of their own employees to monitor and report the department's satisfaction are more likely to take actions that generate measurable results. Remember, positive customer experiences don't happen by chance; they must be consciously designed. The majority of health care organizations have methods to measure patient satisfaction, but not all are successful at converting the data they receive into specific, measurable changes. Surveys provide information, but information alone doesn't create real solutions, nor does it motivate people. Measuring patient satisfaction is like taking the "vital signs" of your organization's service health: It does no good to continue measuring the signs if you don't use the information to diagnose problems and implement a treatment plan.

The measurement task force is charged with turning data into action. But in order to foster ownership and accountability, this task force supports the departments by:

- Gathering data and ensuring that managers know how to retrieve, understand, and report the patient and employee satisfaction data to their staff
- Assisting departments in forming SWAT teams with clearly defined goals, realistic action plans, timelines, and measurable outcomes
- Coaching department heads for successful SWAT implementation
- Becoming a clearinghouse for communicating the cumulative efforts of all SWAT teams

SWAT team process

The Baird Model for Service Excellence is action oriented and engages front line staff in identifying and treating specific problems. Here's how it works: Once you have the data, gather the people who are most likely to influence change at the specific point of service you hope to improve. I recommend working with the department's manager, and requesting that she recruit two or three people from the unit who are willing to serve on a service improvement team. That group will become your SWAT team.

Next, share current satisfaction scores and trends with the SWAT team. Help them to select one or two priorities and set specific goals for improvement. Ask them to provide you with specific plans for their:

- Strategies for improvement
- Work plan, naming the individuals involved; and clarifying what they will do, and when they will do it
- Actions that they will put into place
- Tactics for engaging their peers in making the changes

An example: Your survey shows that the results of your ED's "informed about wait time" question ranks in the 15th percentile, with a mean score of 85. Rather than telling your staff to "Just fix it," you take the SWAT team approach:

1. The manager speaks with your ED staff about the data, and seeks volunteers willing to serve on a service improvement team.

2. The manager, or a member of the measurement team, becomes the leader of the newly formed SWAT team.

3. The SWAT team leader helps the team to begin with the end goal in mind, using a visioning exercise. He asks them to imagine that while in a local coffee shop, they happen to overhear a former patient talking about her wonderful experience in you ED. Then the leader aasks them:

- What is she saying about how she was kept informed?
- What about the experience made it so positive for her?
- How does she describe the staff and their actions?
- In this visioning example, what does being informed look like to the patient?
- What does it sound like to her?
- What does it feel like to her?

4. From the team's responses to these questions, the leader helps team members to formulate a plan that will result in positive changes to a patient experiences in the ED. To do this, they will articulate specific steps and actions that must be taken, the changes in processes that will be necessary.

5. The team writes up their new plan to improve "informed about wait time" scored. The plan will include specifics about getting coworkers on board, standardizing the process, and measuring outcomes once the plan is in place.

6. The SWAT team tests the system and shares the results of the test. If everything is ready, they launch the new process. As new procedures are put into place, the team keeps coworkers informed of the plan's progress; continues to encourage coworkers to remain actively engaged; and considers new approaches.

Goal: To raise the mean score on the ED "informed about wait time" question by 3 points within six months
Strategy: Manage patient expectations by planning for timely interactions and scripted messages.
Work plan: Engage volunteer liaison by January 5, speak with registration staff at Tuesday meeting. Prepare scripts for nurses, registration and volunteers by January 10.
Action: Implement a visual reminder system for staff, showing the last time the patient and family received an update.
Tactics: Target patient interactions every 20 minutes. Discuss at staff meeting, graph out progress on bulletin boards, distribute buttons for staff as a visual reminder.

Formalized process improvement systems like Lean and Six Sigma have helped many health care organizations to improve processes. These process improvements methods can coexist with customer service and culture enhancement initiatives. Even if you don't use Lean, Six Sigma, or another formalized method for process improvement, you can still make great strides in improving satisfaction. The key is to use the data to set clear goals, to take specific actions and to measure results.

One important part of the SWAT process is training SWAT coaches who can support teams in accomplishing their goals. Train these coaches to help teams map out the experiences and create viable plans.

Remember: **If you can measure it, you can move it.** But again: Positive changes only happen by design. Engaging line staff in finding solutions is a grassroots principle of leadership that will help you reach your goals. Using the SWAT approach engages staff closest to the service problem and encourages them to be part of the solution. Although the SET puts process in place, the leaders of each area must carry the processes forward and engage staff in service improvement. It is the department leader who sets the expectation and holds staff accountable for making vital improvements.

3.   *Communication team*

Communication is the thread that connects the internal components of the service excellence team. At the same time, communication maintains the link to the mission, vision and values of the organization. Ideally, the person leading this team will be a seasoned public relations professional. The communication team leader serves as a conduit between the senior leaders and all stakeholder groups. In addition to sending messages about the team's progress, the communication team leader must assist in keeping a clear connection between team function and the organization's goals and strategies. Without this clear message, the team will be viewed as a silo project rather than as an integral part of the strategic plan.

In Chapter One (Priority), I shared a template for a communication plan. This template serves as an excellent guide for planning, and can be incorporated into the duties of the communication team leader.

The duties of the communication team are to:
- Create consistent messages that link the team's functions to the strategic plan, mission and vision
- Communicate customer service information to various stake-- holders
- Keep service standards and success stories visible in various publications and displays
- Support the other four service teams by helping them to create clear communication tools for the recognition program (nomination

forms and instructions), the innovation team (bright ideas forms), measurement (bulletin board design), and standards (pledge form and brochure)

- create a branded look for the service initiative, which will serve as a visual reminder of the organization's commitment to service

4.   Recognition team

Successful recognition programs share certain characteristics: They are sincere, timely, and connected to the organization's standards and vision. A clear connection between standards and recognition is important because it lets people know what they are being recognized for. This connection is often overlooked, even though it seems obvious - in fact, it's amazing how many health care organizations still have the old "Employee of the Month" (EOM) program with no criteria linked to the award.

When we conduct employee focus groups, we often seek feedback about these EOM programs. The typical response is both nonverbal (eye rolling, smirks, and sideways glances at fellow attendees) and verbal ("It's a popularity contest; no one takes it seriously").

If you have an EOM program, either make sure its criteria is woven tightly into your standards for service excellence, or get rid of it. You want every employee to be a stellar performer. Be ready to recognize people when they have exceeded the bar you have set by creating a "Wow!" experience for a patient, family member or coworker.

Making sure that recognition processes are in place and that recognition criteria are tied to the standards are the responsibilities of the recognition team. For example, this team should ensure that processes are in place for peer-to-peer recognition, supervisor-or manager-to-staff recognition, and patient-to-staff recognition. They can create nomination forms that list the organization's standards and ask the nominator to describe how the nominee has exceeded them. This does two things: It connects the situation and the person to the standards, and it helps raise awareness about the behaviors the organization wants to promote. It's human nature to do more of what is recognized and rewarded, so the team must decide what will be rewarded and how it will be recognized.

The recognition team is charged with:
- Putting clear processes and systems in place to link recognition to the standards
- Preparing printed materials related to recognition, including nomination forms and tracking tools
- Drafting instructions about the recognition program
- Creating and supporting scheduled recognition cycles to gather stories of values in action and to publicly recognize individuals
- Building excitement and support for the peer recognition and storytelling to promote service legends

Once these processes are in place, it is the leader's role to make sure that he is modeling recognition and encouraging recognition between peers. In addition to thank-you notes, leaders will help to build a stronger culture of recognition by publicly recognizing staff and giving face-to-face personalized thanks.

5. Innovation team

The innovation task force helps to foster a culture of excellence by engaging everyone in the process of finding solutions to problems. Unlike the old "suggestion box" - where ideas are submitted, never to be seen again - the innovation team ensures that there is a process that will keep people informed about the status of their ideas. This team puts processes in place to elicit ideas, and support their implementation by linking ideas to action-oriented teams.
The innovation team is charged with:
- Putting a process in place that collects, reviews, and triages ideas for implementation

- Establishes a tracking method that includes:
  - * Date idea was submitted
  - * Date reviewed by team
  - * Communication with the person submitting the idea
  - * Person to whom the idea action was delegated
  - * Completion date with department and individuals involved
  - * Recognition for the person or team completing the task

Having all of these processes in place creates structure, but won't guarantee a culture of excellence. It is up to the leaders to promote involvement and use the systems that have been put into place.

Raising the bar: Memorial's processes encourage innovation

Numerous studies have validated the correlation between employee engagement and whether or not they feel that their ideas are valued. And yet, not many organizations have good systems in place for fostering innovation.

Many of us place processes and innovation into two separate categories - one linear, and the other free-flowing. But what if you could employ a process that fosters innovation? That's exactly what Memorial Hospital in South Bend, Indiana, did - and with exemplary results.

Other industries, including manufacturing, retail and hospitality, have historically encouraged innovation to gain a competitive advantage and create shareholder value. In those industries, innovation isn't just encouraged; managers are held accountable for innovation, and have systems that measure, recognize, and sustain innovation. For these industries, innovation is a core competency and is embedded in the culture.

Health care, on the other hand, has not historically placed innovation among our leaders' core competencies. Much to our detriment, our internal silos and isolation from other departments and organizations have limited the diffusion of innovation. But Memorial Hospital is determined to change that.

Memorial's leaders have placed innovation among their most important strategic goals. but their commitment didn't end by writing it in their strategic plan. The leaders committed resources to make innovation a core competency for everyone in the organization. Every new employee attends the "Wow Wizard School" in their very own Innovation Café. That way, Memorial employees learn early in their employment relationship that innovation is a way of life there. It is welcomed and encouraged.

"Health care is plagued with toxic creeping sameness," says Philip Newbold, FACHE, Memorial's president. "We're all claiming the same high quality care, state-of-the-art technology, competitive price and access. We've commoditized the health care industry. In order to stand out from the pack, we must differentiate and innovate."

In 2001, Newbold and a core group of Memorial executives set out to learn everything they could about the world's most innovative companies. Through interviews, research, and site visits, the team learned that the best companies had three common denominators in their core competencies: All were committed to world-class quality, astonishing service, and constant innovation. Learning that many of the most successful companies actually have innovation policies in place came as a surprise to the group.

Memorial's newly formed innovation team realized that, in order to foster innovation in a big way, the organization needed three things: A culture that gives permission to be innovative, competency in building innovation, and the courage to plunge headlong into their commitment. Once they decided to make a clear commitment to innovation, they had to be ready with processes and systems to support that commitment.

The leaders at Memorial created specific processes to foster innovation. Now, starting in new employee orientation, every Memorial employee is encouraged to get engaged in projects that will add value; improve processes and service; help develop, attract or retain talent; or offer a meaningful solution to an important issue.

Memorial has spent thousands of staff hours training managers and staff in innovation. The end result is that the hospital is fostering the culture and building core competencies in innovation throughout the organization. With the motto, "Innovation Everywhere! @ Memorial," innovation is clearly connected to the organization's mission, vision and values, as well as to its core strategies.

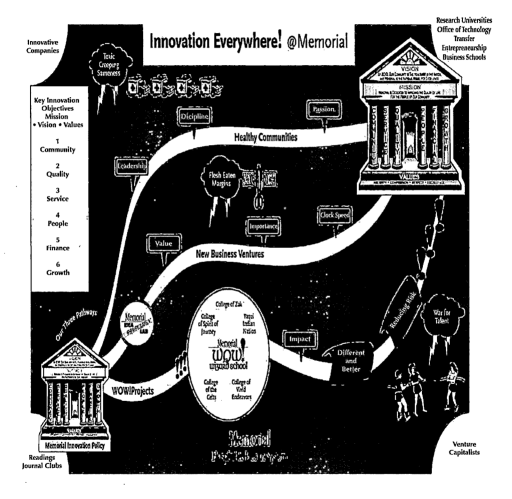

Memorial's process for engaging staff in innovation is visual, experiential, and inspirational. But the beauty of the process is that it is streamlined and simplified, so everyone can understand the importance of innovation as a core competency and can get involved. Memorial has put two processes into place; the approval process, and the Return on Imagination (ROI) process. Rather than forcing people to jump through numerous hoops, Memorial encourages simplicity.

Memorial leaders know that in order to support the case for innovation, the data needs to show a return. In only a few short years, Memorial was able to document a return on investment. But beyond the financial return, Memorial has been able to realize a positive impact on employee engagement.

Memorial clearly demonstrates best practice when it comes to infusing innovation into the culture. The organization's leaders have taken a concept that has not historically been on the health care radar screen, and placed it smack-dab in the middle of daily operations. But without clear, logical processes in place, Memorial's quest for innovation practices could have been just another flavor-of-the-month initiative. Instead, Memorial identified the value of innovation and artfully wove it into the fabric of daily operations.

Process for experience mapping - the moments of truth

Virtually every aspect of the customer experience can benefit from having clear and simple processes in place. There is a certain degree of predictability in the customer experience. Processes provide a framework for handling most situations efficiently. Not only will processes give employees a framework for decision making, they also provide an element of reassurance when employees feel prepared to handle a variety of situations and events.

Many health care organizations are measuring patient satisfaction in an effort to understand the patients' points of view. While those surveys reveal a wealth of information, they sometimes fall short in defining the gaps between patient expectations and actual experiences. It's important for health care organizations to get clear about their customer experiences and moments of truth.

"Moments of truth" can be defined in many ways, but the definition that resonates most strongly with me is the one Susan Keane Baker uses in her book, "Managing Patient Expectations", (1998, Jossey-Bass). Baker defines the moment of truth as "The moment when your patient decides whether or not you are what you say you are."

When do those moments of truth occur? What is the most effective way to find out what a patient experiences at your organization? You can try walking a mile in his shoes - if not physically, then virtually. A concept called "experience mapping" helps health care organizations understand exactly what patients face during countless "moments of truth" in their encounters with the facility.

Experience mapping reveals the mindset behind their patients' actions and expectations. By creating a map, health care providers can begin bridging the chasm between patients' expectations and their actual experiences, and can start to understand what happens when expectations and experiences come together.

Experience mapping also helps providers see that the patient experience actually happens during encounters along a continuum, not the series of silos constructed by internal systems and department politics. A visual way to help providers see where patients encounter obstacles in their care, experience mapping is often a vital step in making process improvements.

We developed the following experience mapping worksheet for our clients to use in evaluating their patients' experiences. The worksheet can be downloaded from our website at:
www.baird-consulting.com.

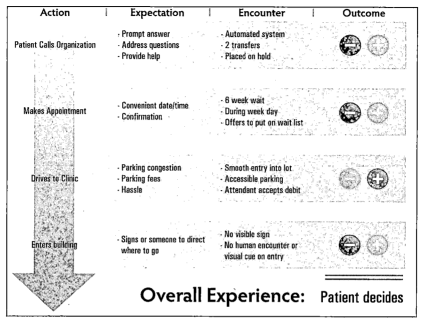

Action	Expectation	Encounter	Outcome
Patient Calls Organization	- Prompt answer - Address questions - Provide help	- Automated system - 2 transfers - Placed on hold	
Makes Appointment	- Convenient date/time - Confirmation	- 6 week wait - During week day - Offers to put on wait list	
Drives to Clinic	- Parking congestion - Parking fees - Hassle	- Smooth entry into lot - Accessible parking - Attendant accepts debit	
Enters building	- Signs or someone to direct where to go	- No visible sign - No human encounter or visual cue on entry	

Overall Experience: Patient decides

© Baird Consulting Inc.   Design credit: Jason Armour

Each column in this chart represents one moment of truth along the patient experience pathway. Each moment of truth can be mapped and analyzed for opportunities for improvement.

Action/need

Every column along an experience pathway starts with an action, taken by either the patient or the provider, to address a need. For example, a patient with a persistent cough needs to call his doctor's office for an appointment, so the doctor can offer reassurance that the cough is treatable, and relieve the patient's symptoms. The action is the phone call to the office for an appointment.

The action can also be initiated by the provider. For example, a nurse needs to take vital signs for diagnostic baseline information. She takes action by entering the exam room and taking the patient's temperature, pulse, and blood pressure. In this case, although the action is taken by the provider, the encounter and resulting experience belongs to the patient.

Expectation

The expectation is the point at which the patient begins to apply his own emotional and experiential filters to the encounter. Each person has a set of expectations for what should happen when he takes action. For example, once the patient decides to call his doctor's office, he may expect that the phone will be answered promptly and that the attendant on the other end will be able to answer his questions and schedule the appointment, promptly and politely.

Patient expectations are subjective and can vary greatly depending on the patient's emotional state and past experiences. For instance, a computer-savvy 20-year-old patient might expect to schedule an appointment via e-mail, while an older patient might expect a friendly voice on the other end of the phone.

Encounter

The encounter is the moment of truth. The patient is aware of what is happening as he makes contact with the organization and begins to compare the encounter to his expectations.

In this example, when the patient calls the clinic, he is actually dialing into an automated system. After two self-selected transfers, he gets a live operator on the phone, and is then placed on hold without his permission. What if he'd been expecting a live attendant on the line? At this point, he makes a judgment. That judgement is the outcome.

Outcome

The outcome is the "verdict" for that specific moment of truth. When the patient compares the actual encounter to his own expectations, he's asking, in effect: "Are you what you say you are?" Subconsciously, as the patient evaluates whether there's a disconnect between his expectations and his actual experience, he applies a positive or negative outcome to each moment of truth. These outcomes have a direct impact on his decision to continue contact with the organization - or not. An experience map can help you to identify best practices, and can also show the organization where negative experiences are occurring.

Experience mapping is valuable not only for improving patient satisfaction, but for determining whether a service is actually ready for market.

Leaders can foster employee engagement by asking them to get involed in the mapping process.

Process for service recovery

We frequently get requests for best practices in service recovery processes. Because this ranks among the most common concerns, I've included some process information here.

We've all experienced bad service at hotels, restaurants, airports and, yes, even health care facilities. But the real test of service excellence comes when a bad experience is swiftly and honestly addressed, and then turned around.

When a customer complains, the service provider has a brief window of opportunity to make or break all chances for satisfactory resolution and, ultimately, future loyalty. What does it take to lead your team in excellent service recovery? The fundamentals are fairly simple, but the leaders' most common challenges are threefold:

1. Training
2. Empowerment
3. Consistent execution of the service recovery process

Service recovery is an opportunity to create raving fans. But it also offers an opportunity for evaluation of the processes or systems that led to the issue in the first place. There are five logical steps in the service recovery process:

*   Anticipating customer needs
*   Acknowledging the customer's concern
*   Apologizing and owning the responsibility

- Offering alternatives
- Making amends

    * Anticipating means understanding customer expecta-
    tions at key points along the experience pathway. If we have
    a clear idea about what the customer expects at each point
    along the experience pathway, we can anticipate and prepare
    for them. When we fail to understand and manage the
    expectations, dissatisfaction occurs. The key to success is
    being able to anticipate the customers' needs at each step,
    and striving to ensure that processes are in place to meet and
    exceed their expectations.

    * Acknowledging the customer's feelings. Service recovery
    begins the moment we recognize that expectations have not
    been met. At that point it is vital that we acknowledge the
    problem and how the customer feels about it. Remember
    that perception is reality. This is not the time to argue and
    explain your postion. It is the time to accept responsibility
    for acting on the customer's complaint. Simply saying, "I can
    understand your point," is an example of acknowledging feel-
    ings.

    * Apologizing. Most of us learned the importance of saying,
    "I'm sorry" as young children. Those two words can diffuse
    anger and bridge an emotional gap between people in a wide
    range of situations. An apology, as simple as it may seem, is
    an important step in moving the situation away from the
    negative and into the positive, action-focused arena. "I'm
    sorry" is one of the most powerful phrases in human com-
    munication. Simply saying, "I'm sorry this happened," can
    de-escalate a negative situation and prevent further prob-
    lems.

* Offering alternatives whenever possible is a method of helping the dissatisfied customer to regain a sense of control.
Rather than telling the person what he or she can't have,
focus on options that are possible. Put the customer back
into the driver's seat.

* Making amends can be as simple as an apology or a follow up
letter, or it may include a small gift or token of appreciation.
But beware; many health care organizations mistake these
tokens for real service recovery. I have seen several hospitals
create "service recovery kits" containing gift certificates and
other "perks" to appease disgruntled customers. The intention may be a sincere desire to compensate the customer for
his inconvenience, but, too often, the issue is dropped there.
Instead, the incident should be seen as an opportunity to
change systems and operations, in order to prevent further
occurrences.

Track service recovery for key opportunities

Complaint management and service recovery go hand in hand
with process improvement.

Keep service recovery logs to record date, time, department,
nature of the complaint, and parties involved. Be sure to record contact information from customers who made the complaints. This
will allow you to contact them and delve further into the situation if
necessary. Gather the data from service recovery logs. Summarize
and find the common denominators.

Frequently, I find organizations keep logs of complaints but
don't actively use the information to prevent further problems. The
key is to mine the information for hidden opportunities. These
opportunities come from the identification of patterns and trends
revealed by the information. Ask questions about the trends. Are
they most common at certain times of day, day of week, shifts, units?

What systems may be contributing to these trends? Use this information to drill down to the root causes of the problems.

Most organizations do not prepare staff adequately for service recovery challenges. When staff members cannot handle customer complaints with confidence, their job satisfaction suffers, and customer satisfaction plummets.

Process improvements related to service recovery:

1. Educate staff about expectations and engage them in anticipating customer needs at each point along the experience pathway.

2. Train staff in communication skills for handling dissatisfied customers, including acknowledging and apologizing when dissatisfaction occurs.

3. Provide staff with options and support for making amends to customers who have encountered disappointing experiences. Make sure they understand what options they can offer and who can assist them in dealing with dissatisfied customers.

4. Anticipate the key issues and needs at each point along the pathway and create processes and systems that ensure that needs are met and exceeded.

5. Examine the customer experience pathway and identify the expectations at each point along the pathway.

Training builds confidence in service recovery

Most health care organizations spend adequate resources training staff for what we know will be inspected. We manage to meet the JCAHO requirements for in-service training, but can't seem to fit some of the most fundamental customer service training into the schedule. The cost of training is the most common barrier cited by managers and senior leaders. But when you calculate the cost of a lost customer, you will quickly realize the value of arming your staff with reliable service recovery tools. Not only do these tools help raise customer satisfaction, they also help raise employee satisfaction and confidence.

Leaders who want to generate a following of raving fans must commit to ongoing training in service recovery. I believe that most employees have a genuine desire to please the customer, but often lack the skills to handle problems. Training and coaching can help increase staff confidence in handling conflict and resolving issues. In addition to training, the culture must support an empowering atmosphere that encourages line staff to solve problems quickly, honestly, and accurately. One essential element of a good service recovery program is a practice of engaging staff in finding solutions to problems. Ask them for ideas about how problem situations can be prevented. Find out what has worked for them in the past, and tap into their combined experience and expertise to build a service recovery process. In so doing, you will be fostering a culture of empowerment and, ultimately, service excellence.

The key to successful service recovery lies in creating an environment where employees feel prepared and empowered to handle whatever comes their way. Only when employees feel prepared and empowered will they be able to view a complaint as a true gift.

Raising the Bar:
Eastern Maine Medical Center decides: Why not ask the patients?

The employees at Eastern Maine Medical Center (EMMC), in Bangor, Maine, have found the secret to delivering customized care. They ask the patient.

EMMC began executing "The Very Good Care Initiative" in 2006. The process is designed to deliver personalized care that will meet or exceed each individual's expectations. The inpatient team that launched the initiative strategically named the program to match the survey language; the survey's highest category is labeled "very good."

"Our staff looked at the old adage, 'Care for each patient the way you would want to be cared for,' and we decided that we needed to do even better than that," said Jill McDonald, vice president of communications and market development. "Care should be delivered the way the patient wants, not according to our preferences, and that means asking the patient to define what is most important."

To achieve their goal of personalized care, EMMC leaders put a process in place. Nurses make rounds each day and ask the patients to define their top three priorities for "very good care." Those priorities are written on a white board in their room so that each caregiver can attend to them throughout the day. In addition to the priorities, they also list the names of the nurse manager and the staff nurse who will be caring for that individual.

According to McDonald, "The priorities patients address are often things like having a smiling nurse, making sure their feet don't get cold, and always having ice water or an extra blanket. Posting the three priorities allows anyone entering the room to check on their status and address problems immediately."

McDonald said the results have been promising. "We have seen a rise in inpatient satisfaction scores, and have noticed a reduction in the number of requests via call lights," she said. "The process has helped to make the staff more aware of patients' individual needs and desires. It all comes down to making sure that the patient feels heard."

The Very Good Care Initiative was so successful on the inpatient units, EMMC has expanded it to their outpatient areas and ED as well. "It's becoming so integrated that patients mention their 'white board' priorities and capitalize 'Very Good Care' in their survey comments. "We are encouraged that this initiative has helped us to step up communication and be more consistent," concludes McDonald. "The outcome is a better experience for our patients."

The Very Good Care Initiative is only one of many reasons that AVATAR International, Inc., a patient satisfaction survey company, has awarded EMMC top honors for five years in a row. Several other process improvements have made a great impact on patient satisfaction over the years.

McDonald has found that there can be a downside to putting new processes in place, however. "When you put a defined process behind the passion for excellence, you sometimes find that people will lose sight of that passion, because they don't like to be legislated on what to say and when. For the sake of consistency, you have to work your way through that." One of the solutions that EMMC found was to involve as many people as possible in process improvement.

When parents of pediatrics patients complained that they didn't always know their child's care providers, a care team came up with a creative solution. At shift change, a ladybug with the nurse's photo is placed on the white board inside the patient's room. This gives the new nurse the opportunity to introduce herself to the family and helps the family to remember each caregiver. This is followed up with a thank-you note given to the family at the time of discharge. The thank-you note is placed in the chart, and during the child's stay, everyone who has cared for the child signs the card.

Staff members in pediatrics led another process change on their unit. The goal was to increase hand-washing compliance. Rather than place signs reminding people to wash hands, staff created posters made up of photos of their own children and posted them throughout the unit above all the sinks. This visual reminder helped staff to remember that they should wash their hands, not only because it is the right thing to do, but because they would want a provider to do this for their own children. This process crossed over on two levels - employee engagement and patient satisfaction.

Process improvement is never-ending. Although patient satisfaction scores are currently at the 96th percentile, EMMC is still striving for improvement. At the top of the list is trying to find ways to reduce noise. McDonald says that they have an inpatient satisfaction team charged with reducing noise levels on the nursing units. Using SHHH (Silent Hospital Help Healing) the team is beginning to make a positive impact. They are sharing information about decibel levels throughout the hospital and suggesting ways to reduce the noise.

"We continue to raise the bar," says McDonald. "It's important for each of us to strive for excellence and hopefully reinforce, at the same time, why we got into this business in the first place."

A few final thoughts on processes

Organizations like the University of Utah Hospital and Clinics, Memorial Hospital of South Bend, and Eastern Maine Medical Center demonstrate that having processes in place helps to unify employees in a common language and approach, whether for innovation or direct patient care. The processes don't have to be complex; in fact, the simpler, the better.

The leader's role in process development is threefold. First, the leader needs to foster a culture that values processes supporting quality, efficiency and a positive patient experience. Second, the leader must ensure that people have the tools in place to make process improvements. Third, the leader must demonstrate how improved processes are supporting the organization's top priorities.

Having clear, simple processes in place will foster an environment that supports employees in their daily work, and encourage their engagement in process improvement.

Leader reflections

Reflect and journal on the following:

- What is the cultural attitude toward processes improvement? Is there resistance to structure? Do people embrace change for the sake of improvement? Are people over-reliant on processes?
- What processes are in place to support a culture of service excellence?
- How does your culture foster process improvement?
- Does the culture promote process improvement in all areas, or is

it primarily dedicated to clinical outcomes?
- How are best practices identified and standardized across the organization? (Are they shared and duplicated, or do they sit in silos?)

Actions

- Review your existing processes for:
  * introducing and reinforcing standards
  * recognizing staff
  * measuring and reporting patient satisfaction data
  * communicating messages with key stakeholders
  * innovation
  * Use experience mapping to identify opportunities for process improvement

Chapter Four

"Efforts and courage are not enough without purpose and direction."

- John F. Kennedy

Anyone in a leadership position must recognize, and come to embrace, the unique purpose of his life.

This is an imperative - regardless of his personal style, his particular profession or the size of his staff. Psychologists now consider a "sense of purpose" a basic human need. We must believe our existence matters - and we must believe that we can offer a positive contribution to the world around us - in order to in order to function effectively as a member of a family, a community, or an organization.

In the work world, a leader must work consistently to nourish his sense of purpose - not only to find greater meaning and richer rewards in his own life's work, but also to be able to help others find the sense of purpose in their own lives. Why is this important? Because if service excellence is an organization's priority, those who actually provide these services must perceive their work as an essential part of a larger whole.

In the health care field, employees must see how the tasks they perform fit into "the greater scheme of things" - whether their responsibility is to clean toilets or to perform open-heart surgery. Leaders can set clear goals and conduct training to help increase focus and competence among employees. But a having sense of purpose is much more than simply knowing what to do and having the skills to do it. By honoring their own sense of purpose, employees become more engaged in their work and more inspired to contribute their time and talent for the greater good. And if they see that their contributions to their organization are consistent with the personal values they hold most dear, they're likely to work harder and with more conviction.

What is a "sense of purpose?" It's been said that "the meaning of life is to find the meaning in life." To me, this quote sums up the very essence of an individual's sense of purpose. But how can a "sense of purpose" be defined?

Perhaps the modern world's best-known exploration of this question comes from the studies of neurologist and psychiatrist Viktor Frankl of Vienna. Arrested by Nazi soldiers shortly after his marriage in 1942, Frankl was transported to a death camp in Bohemia, where his father later starved to death; by 1945, his mother, brother, and wife had all died in the camps. But Frankl would not discover this until after his release. In the meantime, as Frankl was transferred to a second, third, and fourth camp, he managed to survive with two distinct goals in mind: a reunion with his loved ones, and the rewriting of manuscripts of his lost books.

Despite his suffering in the camps, Frankl's avid fascination with human behavior remained, and he noticed something interesting: those prisoners who felt a sense of purpose in their lives - a hope to see a loved one again; a deep religious faith; or a project or task they felt committed to complete - were more likely to survive the brutal conditions than people who had lost hope. His observations led to his development of what he called logotherapy, the term rooted in the Greek word *logos*, or "meaning."

In essence, Frankl theorized that while we cannot avoid suffering, we can choose how we deal with it - and if we can find meaning in our suffering, we can be propelled forward with a new sense of purpose. He detailed his theory in his book, "Man's Search for Meaning," which he wrote in nine days. By the time Frankl died in 1997 at the age of 92, he'd written 32 books, and "Man's Search for Meaning" had sold over nine million copies.

Frankl said, "Life can be pulled by goals just as surely as it can be pushed by drives." What can we learn from Frankl and his observations? Perhaps the stresses of working a modern health care setting cannot be compared to living in a death camp; but the threat of hopelessness is something we all encounter. And Frankl's realization that a purpose, a goal, and the ability to find meaning in an adverse event can certainly be applied to the day-to-day challenges encountered by every staff member in every health care facility.

If a sense of purpose can keep people alive in a death camp, how much more can it impact one's performance in a demanding profession?

Linking to the heart

A sense of purpose really comes down to heart-wiring. My colleague, Kevin Stranberg, and I approach training by focusing on the head, the hands, and the heart. A sense of purpose connects the head (what you know) to the hands (what you do) and to the heart (what you feel). To achieve this, we train to the head (by imparting information and increasing the participant's knowledge about the subject). We train to the hands (by focusing on skill-building). And we train to the heart (by helping the participants to form emotional ties or feelings about their work, which will increase their level of engagement).

When we talk about how to best work with people, we strive to balance our approach to all three elements. This is because we've seen - time and time again - that when training focuses on only the cerebral components of information and skill-building, a work force has a slim chance of becoming engaged and committed to living an organization's mission and vision. Only when their hearts are spoken to and engaged will members of a team be impassioned.

The role of the leader

In the discussion of purpose, I see the leader's role as twofold. Her first task is to find and nourish her own sense of purpose. Her second task is to help her employees find deeper purpose in their work. When the two of these occur simultaneously, the resulting synergy and momentum is palpable.

Consider the fable of the three stonemasons - recorded in the 6th century Rule of St. Benedict, but presenting a timeless truth for today:

A traveler passed three stonemasons hard at work as he entered a city. Two of the men looked haggard and disinterested in their work. But the third man had a radiant smile on his face, energetically humming as he heaved heavy blocks into place. Curious, the traveler asked each man what he was doing. The first man grumbled, "I am sanding down this block of marble." The second man grumbled, "I am prepar-

ing a foundation." But the third man said, with great enthusiasm: "I am building a beautiful cathedral."

Members of any work force must be able to feel they are contributing to something bigger than a "job" to find greater meaning in their work. An effective leader can help them do this. One of the most important things a leader can do for his organization is to help his staff understand the significance of their work - regardless of how mundane their individual tasks may appear.

When employees are able to make this connection - that even their small actions are of consequence - they find that even the most commonplace work takes on a richer meaning. A good leader can provide staff with an explicit "we're making a difference" message - but he also must be able to awaken his staff's intrinsic sense of commitment, by mobilizing each individual's sense of purpose.

*Understand
what to do.*

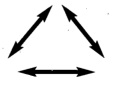

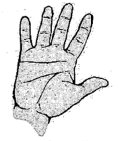

*Want to do the job
and understand
how it connects
to the whole.*

*Have the skills
to do the job.*

Fostering your sense of purpose

A connection to purpose can be fostered through personal reflection. And as a leader, you must seek not only a sense of purpose for your own work - you must help everyone who works around you to do the same. This is crucial, because to form an impassioned and engaged work force, employees must know what they are supposed to do and understand how they are supposed to do it - but they must want to do it, as well.

A leader can't force an employee to become more engaged, of course. To be engaged, or not, is a choice for the individual. But a leader can improve the odds if he can help the employee see how her work contributes to the organization, and how it makes a difference in the lives of others.

You can foster your own sense of purpose by:
- Defining your personal values
- Examining how your personal values fit with your organization's mission, vision and values, and finding significance in your work based on that connection
- Routinely asking yourself routinely, "How does what I do each day make a difference?"
- Helping others to discover and articulate their own sense of purpose

You can foster a connection between your personal sense of purpose and your organization's purpose by linking employees' job functions and duties to your organization's mission, vision and values; and by periodically reviewing these connections, tracing employee contributions to the goals and successes of your organization.

A strong connection to purpose is the glue that binds an individual employee to the work he performs. As I've already mentioned: There is an art and a science to real leadership. Helping others form a strong connection to purpose is one area where the art and science of leadership come together in a big way. The "art" is in helping others to connect to purpose; this starts when the leader takes an inventory of his own attitude and his desire to help others. The "science" is in making that desire a reality. It's not enough for a leader to simply *want* his staff to feel a connection to purpose; he needs to employ some practical tools to make his desire a reality.

Picture this scenario: You walk into one of the busiest units in your hospital. Three housekeepers are working, side by side, mopping the long expanse of hallway. You ask each of them, "What is your job?" The first worker replies, "To do whatever my supervisor puts on my assignment list for the day." The second worker tells you his job is "to clean this department." But the third worker answers, "To create a place where patients want to come for care, where physicians want to practice and where other employees want to work."

The housekeepers of today are like the stonemasons of yesteryear. Which of these three housekeepers is the most engaged, the most connected to the bigger picture of your organization's mission, vision and values? Which one would you want to work with? Which one do you believe would be the productive and thorough? My money would be on the third one - in fact, with an attitude like that, I might want to clone her!

In Chapter One (Priority), I introduced the Priority Pyramid model, which integrates an organization's mission, vision and values with its strategic plan. Just as an organization needs to have a strategy in order to meet its goals, leaders too must have a game plan for achieving their objectives. Do you want to foster a greater sense of purpose among your team members? Don't just wish for it. Take action to make it happen. You can start by asking yourself some questions with answers that will help solidify your approach:

- Where are we going? (This will be your goal.)
- What are we going to do to get there? (This will be your plan.)
- What is my part? (This is your role or job.)

- What's in it for me? (This is your payback or your reward.)
- How will you know how you're doing? (This will be your system of measurement.)

How do you apply what you've learned by asking these questions? Your goal is to help each of your team members to develop a stronger sense of purpose. Your plan might involve steps such as discussing your organization's mission, vision and values during each department meeting, and having a one-on-one discussion with each team member about how his role helps to fulfill the mission. Your payback or reward will be having more engaged, productive staff. And your system to measure success will be observation and data - specifically, you will observe behaviors that demonstrate connection, and you will monitor employee engagement indicators from your employee survey.

When I was a new manager, taking the time to meet with each of my staff members individually to help them identify their personal and professional goals, I was sad to discover that most of the nurses on my team had never been asked these questions. Most of them were grateful to have the chance to articulate their aspirations and desires. But some were astonished, even a little suspicious; after 30 years in the field, I was the first to ask them, "What can I do to help you achieve your goals?"

Instinctively, I knew that if I could help each of them to see the connection between her own values and her work, she would be more engaged and therefore happier in her job. And, as her leader, I could seek opportunities to help her foster her growth in specific areas so she could realize her goals.

That group of nurses showed me that by helping each one of them form a connection between herself, her organization, and her work at hand, I was helping her find greater, richer fulfillment in her job through a connection to purpose.

Personal values intersect with the organization's values

In Chapter One (Priority), I discussed the importance of communicating priorities and making sure that your actions consistently support your words. I talked about ensuring that your organization clearly identifies and communicates its mission, vision and core values. You may need to help your employees to se how their own values intersect with those of your organization to help them develop a stronger connection to purpose.

Some people who are not willing to share their personal value statements may feel safer by making the connection between their job duties and your organizational goals and strategies. As a leader, you can help these individuals intersect their personal values with their job descriptions and the values of your organization.

In the remainder of this chapter, I will share two examples of organizations that have been particularly successful in helping staff members forge stronger connections to their organizations' missions and purposes. Both of these organizations - Park Nicollet Health Services and Presbyterian Healthcare Services - have created specific tools and processes to help employees see these connections. Their approach demonstrates that organizations must develop deliberate, intentional processes to create a climate that enables each employee to form an irrefutable sense of purpose.

Raising the bar:
Park Nicollet helps staff visualize purpose

Park Nicollet Health Services of St. Louis Park, Minnesota does a great job of connecting each person to the job at hand and to the organization's values. The organization created a diagram to help everyone see how these values intersected with each employee's job description:

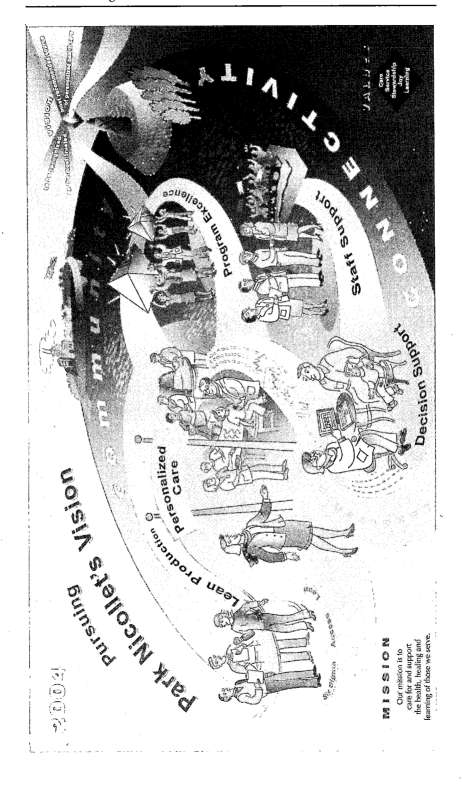

Park Nicollet 2004 Goals and Strategies	Our Department/Site/Unit Goals, Strategies *Leaders: List your area's* *goals and strategies.* *Draw a line to connect them to the* *ogranization's.*	Connecting Your Work *Staff: List your goals and work* *responsibilities.* *Draw a line to connect them to your* *ogranization's and/or department's* *goals and strategies.*

2004 Goals

 Make at least eight systemwide care improvements.

 Meet or exceed patient service expectations, as measured by a Press Ganey overall facility score at the 70th percentile.

 Achieve at least a 3 percent operating margin.

 Continue to exceed national benchmark scores for the employee survey question, "I am proud to work for Park Nicollet Health Services."

 Increase Park Nicollet's peer-reviewed professional and consumer publications.

Grow market share in our service area by one-half of a percentage point, with a focus on key services.

2004 Strategies

Community Connectivity
Engage the community in identifying needs, and raise support to address them.

Personalized Care and Service
Create great experiences for our patients through passionate attention to their personal interests.

Lean Production
Remove waste, waits and errors from our care and support processes.

Supporting Our Staff
Continuously improve a work environment where every person can be successful.

Decision Support
Suppport decision-making by patients, clinicians and leaders through an integrated medical record.

Program Excellence
Achieve consistent value in all programs through a systematic approach to excellence.

Based on Park Nicollet Health Services' 2004 vision poster, with permission

This tool helped Park Nicollet employees see how their organization's objectives were linked to the objectives of their individual departments, and it also helped each individual to tie her own objectives and
work responsibilities to the organization. By visualizing this intercon-
nection, the organization's 8,300 employees, in 25 locations, were able
to see more clearly how their work was making a difference in the lives
of the patients they were serving.

"There is often an epiphany when staff members complete the
visioning exercise, particularly those who are not involved in direct
patient care," says Deidre Spalla, director of human resources at park
Nicollet. "For many of them, it is the first time that they get a clear picture of how their role supports the caregivers and, ultimately, the
patient. It's a beautiful thing."

Any organization that wants to help employees connect to its
organizational mission, vision and values can benefit from using this
type of approach, but when the organization has multiple locations
spread out over a wide geographic region, as Park Nicollet does, such a
tool is even more important. And if low turnover is any indication of
employee engagement, then Park Nicollet is ahead of the curve: The
organization has documented a significant reduction in turnover in the
past five years.

Carol Greenland, vice president of marketing and communications for Park Nicollet, helped develop the visioning tool used throughout the 25-clinic system. "We are a very mission-driven organization,"
Greenland says. "We introduce mission and vision during orientation
and keep talking about it throughout a person's entire employment relationship with us. Overall, I think we do a pretty good job at walking the
talk and putting vision and mission into our daily lives."

Park Nicollet's visioning tool is just one of the many tactics the
organization uses to help individuals stay linked to its mission and
vision. "You just can't post the mission and vision on the wall and
expect that everyone understands how their work connects back to it,"
says Greenland. "We find that constant reminders and regular discussions help to keep that connection top-of-mind. We continually con-

nect the dots for our staff and encourage managers to do the same."

While a connection to purpose is often considered a personal issue, managers play an integral role in helping their staff make that connection. Managers at Park Nicollet were provided with a toolkit to help them present the visioning tool to their departments as a group, and to each individual as well. In both group and individual discussions, the visioning tool has been enormously successful in helping people gain a greater appreciation for exactly how individuals and departments contribute to the organization's goals and strategic plan.

"We have used this tool or various iterations of it for the past five years," explains Greenland. The latest version, she says, is on the back of a poster that features a yearlong calendar. Each month on the calendar highlights a particular team and shows how its projects or achievements contribute to the organization's strategic plan.

"It's one thing to understand how each of us fits into the organizational plan, but it is another to help teams to see their fit as well," Greenland says. "Linking team goals to organizational goals is just one more way we are fostering better alignment. And with all the pressures placed on managers today, alignment becomes more important than ever."

Greenland points out that competing priorities threaten the organization's culture by making it increasingly difficult for managers to give the time and attention needed to lead their teams to optimal performance. "Managers have so many demands on them," she says. "If it's not JCAHO, it's safety issues, quality and patient satisfaction. Those challenges are very real and continually pull at the managers in addition to all of the daily demands of leadership."

Greenland says the effort will be ongoing "because we know that the leaders who successfully engage their team members will have lower turnover, higher performance and higher scores on both the employee satisfaction surveys and on the patient satisfaction surveys. There are a lot of ways to engage people and this tool is only one, but it is very visual and very effective."

Raising the bar:
Presbyterian creates the EGG

Presbyterian Healthcare Services in Albuquerque, New Mexico does a stellar job in helping each of its 9,500 employees form a personal connection to the organization. Similar to the approach taken by Park Nicollet, Presbyterian has developed a visual tool that assists each employee in linking his job to the purpose, vision, values and strategies which are described in the organizational EGG. But even beyond the visual tool, Presbyterian's success is due to a process the organization had put in place to make that goal a reality.

Presbyterian developed the EGG and was already on track to earn the 2000 Malcom Baldridge National Quality journey when the organization first developed the individual "job Egg," according to Renee Reimer, Presbyterian's former Vice President of Human Resources. The organizational EGG is a visual representation showing "standards" at the center (as the yolk), surrounded by "purpose," "vision," "values" and "strategies" linked by a sense of mission.

Presbyterian Organizational EGG

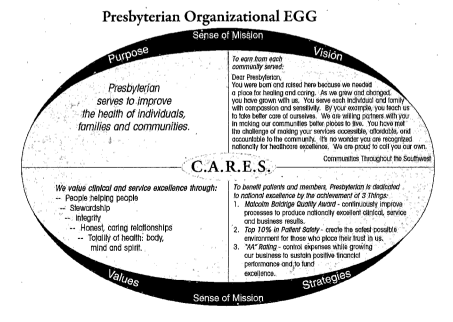

@Presbyterian Healthcare Services

"We wanted to find a simple and memorable way for each employee to see how his job supports and aligns with the organizational purpose," explains Reimer. "After a few iterations we developed a simple visual that helps each individual form a connection to purpose."

Senior leaders knew that in order to achieve excellence according to the highest national standards, every employee would have to see how he or she was aligned with that goal. "But that alignment won't happen by chance," she says. "It will only occur by designing a very deliberate process."

According to Michelle Campbell, vice president of marketing for Presbyterian, "Every new employee is introduced to the Job Egg during orientation. They are asked to review and reflect on the organizational EGG and consider how his or her job fits within that."

Each employee is expected to share her Egg with her supervisor within the first 30 to 90 days of employment and keep the Egg where others can see it, such as on an office door or a bulletin board. The symbol is on the back of each employee name badge, and is even used as a screen saver on the organization's computer screens.

"Nurses on a particular unit may opt to develop a nursing Egg together," she says, "But everyone has an Egg." And it's not a "one-time thing," she says. Presbyterian has a process to refresh the Egg regularly, so as employees evolve and grow in their work, they can look at their Eggs with a fresh perspective and make changes if necessary.

Presbyterian's standards are called CARES behaviors. CARES (an acronym for Continuous learning, Accountability, Respect and respond, Environment of health, and Superior outcomes), helps each employee identify which behaviors are most pertinent to her job. "For example, one year a person's focus may be on accountability and the next year, based on what is happening for that person, he may refresh the focus to be continuous learning or another standard," she says. "We feel that unless employees talk about what standards have to do with their jobs, they don't feel as 'real.' Initially, this was a forced activity. But overwhelmingly, people responded that it helped them to see how they connect to purpose."

As an example, Reimer explains that someone in housekeeping or food service may initially see his job as focused on a list of tasks at hand. "But when he puts his duties in context of an organizational Egg, he sees himself as part of whole," she says. "It's pretty powerful."

One way Presbyterian engages employees in creating their Job Eggs is by having each of them write a hypothetical letter that they'd like to receive from one of their customers, clarifying how their work has made a difference. This process mirrors the letter within the vision quadrant of the organizational EGG. It's a great way to introduce our new employees to our culture and help them to see how they fit into the grand scheme of things," says Campbell.

The letter concept is how Presbyterian articulates the organization's vision and is even carried over to their website. Under the heading, "Our Commitment to You," is the text: "We want to earn this symbolic letter from the communities we serve." The following letter is posted:

> Dear Presbyterian,
>
> You were born and raised here because we needed a place for healing and caring. As we grew and changed, you have grown with us. You serve each individual and family with compassion and sensitivity. By your example, you teach us to take better care of ourselves. We are willing partners with you in making our communities better places to live. You have met the challenge of making your services accessible, affordable, and accountable to the community. It's no wonder you are recognized nationally for healthcare excellence. We are proud to call you our own.
>
> Communities Throughout the Southwest

Presbyterian believes that sharing stories from patients and members is a vital element of their culture and one that helps maintain a connection to purpose. Leaders share stories about connection to purpose during their quarterly Leadership Development Institutes (a result of their work with The Studer Group). Most of the stories are framed around why they got into the health care profession and how they strive to make a difference. Department leaders are also encouraged to share connection to purpose stories during meetings as a way to bring the connections to life.

There is a measurable bottom-line impact from helping individuals form a connection to purpose. Presbyterian has an index of engagement, loyalty and retention. In a market with a limited pool of employees, Presbyterian had a vested interest in reducing turnover. Presbyterian documented that a one percent turnover translated into $1.5 million. By decreasing turnover, Presbyterian could demonstrate significant cost savings. By helping individuals develop a stronger sense of purpose, the organization hoped to increase engagement and longevity. And it has. Since 1999, Presbyterian has reduced turnover from 30 percent to 16 percent.

Job Egg links each person to purpose

The Job Egg at Presbyterian was designed to link people and their roles to purpose. The alignment gives clarity and helps to increase job satisfaction. For many people employed in health care settings, seeing a direct connection to the organization's mission and vision is obvious. For others, finding the connection to purpose takes deeper reflection.

Jana Burdick is the director of Health Plan Benefit Administration and System Configuration for Presbyterian Health Plan. "Working in the health plan business unit of our system, I'm not involved in direct patient care, (and I don't) work with the care providers directly," she says. "But I never lose sight of my purpose in the organization."

Burdick describes how the Presbyterian Job Egg was designed to help everyone - including herself - to stay connected to purpose. "At each quarterly Leadership Development Institute meeting, someone is asked to share his or her individual connection to purpose," she says. "This is usually something that happened in our personal lives that shows us how we connect to Presbyterian's purpose."

When Burdick was asked to speak at the quarterly Leadership Development Institute, she shared a personal story about her brother, who had been injured in a severe accident a few years before. "I wasn't able to provide hands-on care, but my role was to help him navigate the insurance so that he could get his claims processed and not have worry about coverage," she says. "He would have been overwhelmed if he had to face the financial demands."

The experience, says Burdick, taught her a great deal about the value the health plan department brings to the organization and its customers, even though "our department is buried deep down in the organization. We never have a chance to come face to face with the members, patients or providers, but we still need to understand that when we make a mistake we have a deep and profound effect on the customers' experience."

Burdick knows that claim problems create big problems for the individual member as well as for the organization as a whole. "I see my role as protecting the financial resources of the organization so that we can make sure that the right amount of money goes to provide care and that information is processed efficiently to prevent hassle for the patient," she says. The Job Egg "is a concise, one-page picture of how we connect to Presbyterian's purpose. On days when things are tough, I look at my Egg and remember why I am here."

Burdick praises CEO Jim Hinton for his belief in helping employees connect to the purpose, vision and values of Presbyterian. "He makes it very clear that if you can't buy into the mission, vision and values, you don't have a place here."

Jana Burdick's Job EGG

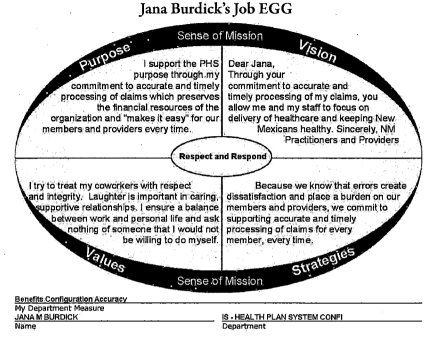

Sense of Mission

I support the PHS purpose through my commitment to accurate and timely processing of claims which preserves the financial resources of the organization and "makes it easy" for our members and providers every time.	Dear Jana, Through your commitment to accurate and timely processing of my claims, you allow me and my staff to focus on delivery of healthcare and keeping New Mexicans healthy. Sincerely, NM Practitioners and Providers

Respect and Respond

I try to treat my coworkers with respect and integrity. Laughter is important in caring, supportive relationships. I ensure a balance between work and personal life and ask nothing of someone that I would not be willing to do myself.	Because we know that errors create dissatisfaction and place a burden on our members and providers, we commit to supporting accurate and timely processing of claims for every member, every time.

Sense of Mission

Benefits Configuration Accuracy
My Department Measure

JANA M BURDICK	IS - HEALTH PLAN SYSTEM CONFI
Name	Department

When Christina Vigil joined Presbyterian as an in-house attorney, she had some difficulty acclimating to the health care arena from the environment of a traditional legal practice. "The whole language of health care and health care quality is unique to the industry," Vigil explains. "But the very essence of what I do is based on communication, so I focus a lot on what is communicated and how it is communicated. So for me, our Job Egg is a means and method of communicating our culture through a common language."

A common form of communication, she says, is important in an organization because it helps build a common purpose for teams and brings employees together to a common point. "It's like a team branding that gives us team spirit, sort of like the fraternal handshake or symbol that says, 'You are part of this team,'" she says. "A shared identity and shared sense of contribution - that can be priceless."

Vigil also talks about her experience of sharing her individual story with other Presbyterian Presbyterian employees, and, like Burdick, she found the experience a meaningful and fulfilling one. First, Vigil had to admit that she hadn't joined Presbyterian "with a passion for healing as a driving force. My connection to purpose isn't how I got to Presbyterian, but it is why I stay. I stay because of the moving stories that I have come across that resonate with me. I stay because I can see how my work makes a difference in the lives of others."

As an attorney, Vigil's job is to provide risk management and work with contracts, but she's discovered her job "is so much more. What I do in the course of my work, and what people think I do, are often quite different."

One particular event, she says, "has been a hallmark in my personal transformation." That night, while nursing her newborn son, Vigil received a phone call from the labor and delivery department. A 17-year-old woman on the unit had just given birth; anemic and bleeding badly, she needed a blood transfusion to save her life. But the young mother refused the transfusion for religious reasons. Vigil's task was to get a court order for the transfusion.

"I handed my sleeping baby off to my husband and raced to the hospital gathering information from the nurses while driving," she says. "I called the judge and got the necessary order. As soon as I got the word from the judge, I called the nursing staff to let them know that they could begin the lifesaving transfusion."

But the order had come too late. The young mother had already died. "I fell apart," Vigil says. "I was stunned and crushed that it had been too late. Her death was very hard on all of us, the nurses, the physician and me. We did a debriefing afterward and confirmed that we had done everything that could have been done."

But the story didn't end that night. Two years later, Vigil received a call from the OB department, telling her that the father of the deceased teen wanted to talk to the nurses who had been present at the time. Not surprisingly, Vigil found, "the attorney side of my brain ... thinking, 'Uh-oh. He's gathering information for a lawsuit.'"

When Vigil called the father, he explained that he'd been in the hospital - but not at his daughter's bedside - when she had died, and he "just wanted to know what happened." It took the staff a couple of days to locate the nurses that had been in the room at the time of her death - but once they did, Vigil was in for a surprise.

"From out of the blue, one of the nurses called me and told me in detail about this young woman's last moments," says Vigil. Vigil called the father to relay the story, and that's when she discovered the father's true motivation. "I told him that just before his daughter passed away, this nurse had held the baby up to his daughter's face," Vigil recalls. "His daughter had nodded, indicating that she clearly saw her newborn baby. There was a long silence on the phone after I told this man what I knew of his daughter's last moments. And then he began to weep openly. He said, 'I can't tell you what this means to me. Everyone is always asking me if she ever saw her baby, and I never knew. Now I know. This gives me such peace.'"

Vigil hadn't realized that this bit of information was what the father needed. "I was speechless," she says. "I was in shock. I don't know if it was coincidence or grace that the nurses kept trying until they found someone with a direct memory of this man's daughter, but they did. They found exactly what would bring some peace and closure for this man."

Situations like these continue to reaffirm Vigil's "connection a greater purpose each and every day," she says. "So, when I get up in the morning, especially during busy, overwhelming times, it is stories like these that make me love what I do."

Vigil created her Job Egg, "not with my job description in mind, (but) with this, and the numerous other stories, in my heart. I've learned that not all my work is about the regulatory stuff. It's about how we treat the patients. I've learned that what I do can have a profound effect on people."

Fostering a personal sense of purpose is an inside job. But when a culture promotes personal reflection and integration with an organization's values, the long-term effects on both the individual and the organization are significant. In order to make a connection meaningful and sustaining, leaders must be crystal clear about their organization's priorities. Beginning a process to help people connect to purpose without clear priorities, vision, and values is like trying to build a skyscraper on sand. You need solid footing in order to sustain your efforts.

Ask yourself if you have established and effectively communicated priorities. Determine if you have the right people in place as well as the processes to support their efforts. Once you have these three things in place, it's time to weave them together through a connection to purpose.

As the stories from Park Nicollet and Presbyterian Healthcare System demonstrate, an organization must have processes in place to engage employees' mindset about their connection to the organization's purpose, right from the beginning. And organizations that are successful in making these connections have a much better prognosis for establishing and sustaining employee and patient loyalty over time.

"An empowered organization is one in which individuals have the knowledge, skill, desire, and opportunity to personally succeed in a way that leads to collective organizational success."

- Steven Covey, "Principle-Centered Leadership"

Leader reflections
Reflect and journal on the following:

- List your core personal values.
- Ask yourself how you link your personal values to your job.
- Ask yourself what, if anything, causes a "disconnect" between your values and your work.
- Consider your state of mind and level of productivity and engagement when you feel strongly connected to the organization's purpose.
- Consider your state of mind and level of productivity and engagement when you felt disconnected from the organization's purpose.

- Ask yourself what situations are most likely to cause you to feel disconnected from the organization's purpose.

Actions:
- Review ways in which your organization helps to foster each individual's sense of purpose.
- Identify at least two new ideas for helping others form a stronger connection to purpose.
- After reviewing the examples from Park Nicollet and Presbyterian Healthcare Service, consider how your organization can weave connection-to-purpose into the fabric of the culture. Consider these questions as a litmus test:
    * How are team activities connected to the strategic plan?
    * How are the individual jobs connected to organizational vision?

Chapter Five

"Passion is the robust, constant energizing force that drives you toward a goal that others see as impossible."

> *- Dr. Tom Royer, CEO, CHRISTUS Health*

"Only passions, great passions, can elevate the soul to great things."

> *- Denis Diderot*

In 1963, passion fueled Martin Luther King Jr. to stand on the steps of the Lincoln Memorial and share his "dream" before 200,000 civil rights supporters. In 1945, passion spurred Winston Churchill on as he led Britain to victory against the Axis Powers.

In the 1850s, passion - not just "the lamp" - illuminated Florence Nightengale's path as she cared for wounded soldiers during the Crimean War. At a time when nurses were treated with distain and the need for sanitation was unknown, Nightengale's tireless work increased the soldiers' survival rates, and helped transform nursing into a "respectible" profession.

Today, in the health care field, the need for passion continues. Passion drives health care leaders to "raise the bar," striving to improve their organizations and move them from good to great.

Ask a group of people to name the greatest leaders of all time and you will hear the names of magnetic, impassioned people who inspired others - not just with logic and data, but with fire-in-the-belly passion. Great leaders are energized by their passion and emit an energy that invites - no, draws - others to them in common pursuit of a cause.

I firmly believe that in order to be effective, leaders must have passion for their work - a passion that permeates every crevice of their organization. So I grappled with the decision of whether or not to place this chapter in the beginning of the book or at the end. After all, doesn't the subtitle include the word "passion?" But I finally decided to address passion in this final chapter. This is because I've learned that even the most passionate leaders still need clear priorities; the right people; efficient processes; and a well-defined purpose to drive a successful organization. When all these elements are combined, the results are phenomenal.

Some leaders who read this book are already passion-driven, but they need more structure to fulfill their goals. Other leaders who are more methodical may read this book and discover that they need to infuse passion into their plans to improve their success. Either way, the priority, people, process and purpose are the foundational blocks of a successful organization, and the passion is the mortar that holds these blocks firmly in place.

Are you an inspired leader? Do you believe so strongly in your mission and vision that nothing - I mean nothing - will keep you from reaching your goals? Impassioned leaders don't always have the title that identifies them as such. After all, passion doesn't always have to manifest itself in flamboyant, charismatic and public displays or soliloquies as those cited above. Sometimes the most passionate leadership comes from quiet perseverance fueled by a belief in - and love for - the task at hand. Mother Teresa of Kolkata is not remembered for charismatic speeches, but rather for her quiet, persistent pursuit of humanitarian works.

And yet, the impassioned individual can be transformed by his own passion, and become capable of stretching beyond his comfort zone for the sake of his cause. I've been surprised more than once by seemingly mild-mannered individuals who, when discussing things they're passionate about, become persuasive, animated orators.

In the July 1999 issue of Innovative Leader, the speaker, consultant and author Chip R. Bell writes: "We have missed the boat on what it means to be leader. The world ... the organization ... and the situation offer far more 'predictable' than is predictably required. The truth is that *rationality* oozes from the seams of every business encounter. Leaders don't have to bring order, sanity, rationality or logic. Every dimension of business life reeks with those qualities. Sane leaders foster insane passion. Memorable leaders call up in each of us a visit with the raggedy edge of brilliance and the out-of-the-way corner of genius. When we feel inspired, incensed, ennobled ... we have visited the magical realm of passion. And, we typically return from that realm renewed, revitalized ... and slightly revolted. The bittersweet taste of unexplored talent is the byproduct of a passion projection into that world. And, when a leader has had a hand in that flight, there is at once a sense of security wedded to an otherwise solitary search."

"A leader does not deserve the name unless he is willing occasionally to stand alone."

- Henry A. Kissenger

Of course, passion without direction and visible action can become misguided, disorganized or chaotic, leaving managers scrambling to understand priorities. "You can't 'policy' peoples' hearts," Quint Studer, founder of the Studer Group and author of "Hardwiring Service Excellence," once told me. He is right. You can't beat passion and a sense of purpose into people simply by showing metrics and pushing goals.

So how do you engage people in making service a part of who they are as individuals and who you are as an organization? Passion is a form of energy that attracts more of the same. So if you want an impassioned work force, you need to fuel your personal passion for the work that you do. After all, you've chosen to work in the health care industry - not in manufacturing, ditch-digging or waste management. The field of health care is exciting, with the act of caring for human beings at its very core. And it is an honor to care for others.

It seems that certain people's personalities include a natural predisposition for passion. Some believe that people are either passionate or they're not. But I disagree. Without entering into a discussion about the relative importance of genetics vs. environment, I'll say that I believe that passion can be developed and fostered, like any other personal characteristic. And through reflection and introspection, that passion will continue to grow.

But it may take practice. And it may take perseverance to withstand the inevitable bad days and dry spells. How do you keep a clear picture of the importance of your work - and keep your employees engaged - during these times? By remembering your love for what you do and your unwavering belief in your work. If you continue to lead with passion regardless of the challenges of the moment, your followers will not only learn from you, they will emulate your passion and your culture will resonate with that energy.

Give your passion a tune-up

Like a flame, passion needs fuel and the proper environment in order to be sustained. You can increase a sense of passion within yourself. How? Find things that make you passionate. Read about them; listen to others who are passionate about the same issue. Read or watch speeches delivered by impassioned leaders. If you want to be more passionate, you must expose yourself to increased doses of the same.

Passion is personal

There is a down side to passion. If you care deeply about your work, about the people around you and about how your patients feel about your organization, you will also care deeply when things go wrong. When good people leave your organization, or the quality of your employees' work has been sub par, or a patient is dissatisfied, it will become personal for you. You'll be bound to feel these disappointments with greater depth than you would if you were detached.

But there's another side of that coin. When you connect your personal values to your work, you'll feel the joys and triumphs with greater depth as well. The people around you will feel that energy. And that's a beautiful thing.

Years ago, I worked with a CEO after a toddler had died in his hospital's emergency department. He'd contacted me to help him manage the communication surrounding the event. During our meeting he methodically described the "sentinel event" to give me the background that I needed in order to help them. I knew that the clinical staff was holding a debriefing session and doing a root-cause analysis. As the communications expert, I did the usual crisis communication planning and discussed plans for what to say to staff and any potential media that might inquire. During the process, the

CEO had calmly discussed his thoughts.

But as we drew our meeting to a close, I asked, "Who is talking to the parents?" The physician and the clergy who had worked with the family during the incident would take care of that, the CEO told me. I asked him if he would consider calling the parents and extending his personal condolences. He turned to me, tears welling up in his eyes. "I can't make that call," he answered. "I just wouldn't have the words to express how awful I feel. I know I shouldn't admit this, but I take this kind of thing personally. The work that we do here is so important to every person that comes through these doors. It just tears me apart when we fail someone even if circumstances are beyond our control."

I could see the depth of his grief and disappointment, and I told him that it was that level of caring that made me want to work with him. His reaction made him human and reminded me that we shared a passion and the core values that made us want to do the kind of work that we do. As I left the meeting, I asked that he "just think about it." I never brought it up to him again, because I felt that his decision about making the call was a personal one.

About a week later, the CEO called me into his office and showed me a letter. It took a moment for me to realize that it was from the parents whose child who had died in the ED. They wrote that they knew the ED team had done everything in their power to save their daughter, and that they had no doubt about how deeply everyone there cared about their loss. They wrote that they were glad to know that this hospital and staff were in their community to serve their family. Last, they wrote about how much it had meant to them that the CEO had called them personally to offer his condolences: "Your call made us feel like everyone in your hospital really cares about us. Thank you for being there."

Talk about values in action! In spite of his own emotions, this CEO made the call. This is what passion looks like. You can talk about passion to your staff or you can show them what it looks like: Being real. Being human is what living your passion is all about. And when your employees see this, they want to be more like that as well. They want to learn how to connect on a deeper level with patients and families.

Because stories resonate differently than factual summaries, storytelling is a skill that helps infuse passion throughout an organization. In this case, I suggested that the CEO read the letter out loud at an employee forum. At first, he worried that it would look like he was patting himself on the back, but I assured him it was a story worth telling and let him make his own decision.

He did read the letter to the ED staff, I learned later, and there hadn't been a dry eye in the room. These were the very people who had struggled through the night trying to save the little girl. They had skin in the game; they were invested; they were feeling the pain. But when they heard what the parents had written about the CEO, the CEO suddenly became "one of them." He was one of the team, one of those who had grieved the loss of a patient.

As the CEO was leaving the staff meeting, one of the nurses put her arms around him. "Thank you for calling those parents for us," she said. "It shows that you care as much as we do. Sometimes we forget that we're not alone. We may be at the bedside, but you care as much as we do." And with that, the entire staff stood up and applauded.

This is the stuff that legends are made of. The CEO could write newsletter articles and give speeches about his great sense of passion - but by sharing this story he was able to demonstrate his passion in a manner that resonated deeply with every person who would hear the story.

How many times do you think that story was shared with other staff? Countless times. In fact, the ED director later told the story during a management training session. "You cannot measure the impact that this had on the staff," she'd told the trainees. "Every one of us feels proud to work here and proud to have a CEO that cares as much as we do."

The CEO had communicated his passion through his actions, and not just his words. As a leader, you can, too. The word "communicate" comes from the Latin root meaning "community;" therefore, your efforts to communicate organizational mission, vision and values will build a sense of community with a common focus and passion.

Storytelling is an invaluable skill that leaders can use in a multitude of situations. Helping staff overcome conflict, promoting your vision or engaging jaded colleagues are just a few of the situations where a well-timed story can shift the mood. We may say we just want the facts, but the truth is that we mere mortals are moved by emotions more than cognition.

After I read Annette Simmons' book, "Whoever Tells the Best Story Wins - How to Use Your Own Stories to Communicate with Power and Impact" (2007, AMACOM Books), I just knew I had to meet her. I discovered that Simmons speaks as eloquently as she writes, and that she delivers a great message for leaders who want to lead with more passion. My interview with her left me with a much deeper understanding of how storytelling instills greater passion.

"It isn't just the listener who grows during storytelling," explains Simmons. "The person telling the story grows too. What you learn telling your own stories actually sticks with you on a deeper level, which strengthens your convictions even further."

Storytelling also helps put values into action. "Values mean different things to different people," says Simmons. "Because values are so subjective, you need to validate them with stories which bring them to life. The listener will get the spirit of it."

Simmons calls it "a bit short-sighted" to assume that when management prints a list of values, employees will automatically understand their meaning. "For example," she says, "the word 'integrity' cannot be defined in a meaningful way without a story. Your story, your behavior set the bar and everyone is watching. But of course they can't see you in every move that you make. You may value respect, but unless you tell a story about how you show respect, people won't really get it. It's not arrogant to tell a story about respect and how you show respect. That story tells the listener everything they need to know about the culture. You cannot create policies to force values. It makes people stop thinking. You can't mandate culture. You have to live it and tell it through stories. Stories became the policy manual."

Because values and service standards can be made more "real" to staff through stories, Simmons suggests that leaders share DVDs with stories about caregivers and patients with staff at least once per quarter. "Circulating these stories is more powerful than metrics," she says.

Simmons offers some great insight into the link between health care, passion and leadership. "Health care leaders, in particular, need to consider the kinds of people who choose to go into health care in the first place," she says. "Many of our health care workers are truly passionate about caring for their patients. If those passion-driven employees don't have what they need to serve their patients well, or if they feel they hit roadblocks delivering passionate care, they will be equally passionate about the negatives as well."

These are the employees who will "buck the system" to improve patient care; if their efforts aren't successful, they will leave for an organization or department more in sync with their personal values. But these are the people who "can be great assets to the organization if their stories are heard," Simmons says. "Help them tell their stories and honor their passion for patient care."

Based on Simmons' input, I believe it's safe to say that passionate people stir things up by asking questions, challenging the status quo and seeking clarification. And that's okay. In fact, it's desirable. Some leaders get defensive with questioning and challenging, but if they recognize these behaviors are signs of active engagement and passion for the cause, they'll see it's not all bad. Maybe we need to learn a lesson: We need to get comfortable with a little discomfort.

Simmons warns that there is danger in telling ourselves and our employees that "it's just business, it's not personal." She says that by de-personalizing the work, we are squelching our own passion as well as theirs.

"Passionate people get frustrated when they cannot deliver the level of care that they feel is essential. If you deny the validity of their frustration, you are helping them to retreat into cynicism and apathy," says Simmons. In every business, but particularly in health care, we need to be rebuilding and rejuvenating passion and accommodating the need for passion on a daily basis.

Simmons' book on storytelling contains tools and exercises to help leaders become better storytellers. By giving her readers writing cues, she helps them to first define their own values, then to find stories that illustrate those values. She offers lessons on crafting and delivering five different categories of stories:

- *Who-I-Am Stories*, which help leaders reveal who they are as individuals in order to build trust
- *Teaching Stories*, which share experiences and the lessons learned from them. Telling such stories delivers a much stronger and more memorable message than simply offering advice
- *Vision Stories*, which help others reframe today's difficulties as being worthwhile in light of the prospect of an exciting future
- *Values-in-Action Stories*, which help people understand subjective values. People comprehend values more clearly when a leader can paint a picture of what the value looks like in action
- I-*Know-What-You-Are-Thinking Stories*, which are particularly effective when leaders are faced with opposition and cynicism. This approach helps others to share their suspicions, giving the leader the opportunity to validate and dispel objections

As a leader, you can encourage others to tell stories by telling your own stories and then providing openings for others to share their stories as well. To get the process rolling, you can ask open-ended questions, such as:

- What happened?
- Who was there?
- What was going through your mind?

Simmons warns that if you probe further discussion by asking, "How did you feel?" you may people down without meaning to. "Instead," Simmons advises, "take them back to the moment in time."

Leaders who want to build trust can tell stories about "a time when I blew it." According to Simmons, "You can build trust exponentially in three minutes flat with this type of story. People love to hear humility stories. When you share your mistakes, you become more human, more real, more like them."

I find that when I tell this type of humility story, I can also tie the situation to my values and show how my mistake actually helped strengthen my values in some way. "Lessons learned" stories will stick with people longer, and leave a stronger impression, than a list of values in a document.

Raising the bar:
Good Samaritan's impassioned stories build impassioned work force

Larry Beck, the president and CEO of Good Samaritan Hospital in Baltimore, Maryland, is one of health care's most passionate leaders. Beck feels that storytelling is a vital tool in building a culture of excellence.

"Our story is really that of the Good Samaritan from the Bible," he says. "I tell that story during orientation in order to make a clear and impassioned connection to our mission. We stress that all of us, regardless of our positions, need to reach out and help others in a time of need. We start communicating this in new employee orientation and continue telling stories of excellence day after day. Storytelling is a great way to reach people. Everyone learns powerful messages from stories."

Beck understands that passion alone won't help him to create a culture of service excellence. "I could have all the passion in the world, but I need the right tools in place in order to put that passion into practice," he says. "It's like gardening. You may want a beautiful garden but without the right tools you'll be down there digging with your hands and probably won't get too far. A passionate leader needs to be able to operationalize his plan."

Beck sees the value of his passion in making the culture a positive one, but he also knows that tools and structure are necessary for success. Beck credits several sources for helping develop the best tools for putting passion in to practice. Among them are The Ritz-Carlton; Baptist Health; the Studer Group; and the book, "Good to Great: Why Some Companies Make the Leap... and Others Don't," by Jim Collins.

"We define culture as 'What you do when no one else is looking,'" Beck says. Storytelling is one tool he uses to unify 3,000 employees and medical staff under a common value system. Although the organization currently scores very well in patient satisfaction, Beck will be the first to admit that it's on a continuous journey of improvement.

Leaders like Beck know that an impassioned culture is an engaged culture. Think about the word "engaged." No matter in which context it is used, you'll find that the word is always associated with passion.

Think about the following:

- What energizes you at work?
- What makes you want to go to work?
- What keeps you going on a busy day?
- Even when you are exhausted, what is it about your work that makes you still feel it is worthwhile?

I think it is also very important to identify your energy zappers so that you can figure out how to avoid them, or how to work through the people and things that sap your passion.

In his July 1999 article mentioned above, Bell urges leaders to rethink their passion. He asks, "Why are you here, in this role, at this time? What difference will your being here make? What legacy will you leave behind? Will you be forgotten for what you maintained or remembered for what you added? Imposing mountains are climbed, culture-changing movements are started, and breakthrough miracles are sparked by leaders who took the governors off rationalism and prudence, letting their spirit ascend from within."

The bottom line is this: Passionate leaders foster passionate teams. In turn, passionate teams foster passionately loyal customers.

Raising the bar:
Avatar International honors the 'Bold, Daring, and a Little Gutsy'

Leading with passion takes guts. A passionate leader knows that challenging the status quo and doing the right thing isn't always easy. When Avatar International, Inc. – a survey vendor that helps hospitals measure patient satisfaction and promote quality improvements began honoring client hospitals for innovation in customer service, it became apparent that innovation was most effective at the hands of bold, daring and gutsy leaders. "It wasn't so much what they did, but how they did it," says Beth Everett, MPH, RD, the vice president of Avatar International, Inc. "These leaders were innovators fueled by passion and persistence. For that reason, we made 'Bold, Daring and a Little Gutsy' a criteria for our innovation awards."

Everett says that innovators:

• Do what others say can't be done
• Do what others are not doing

- Go where others haven't gone
- Overcome barriers
- Create energy to keep going

I agree with Everett's definition of great innovators, and I believe the same characteristics apply to passionate leaders. Passionate leaders aren't daunted when others tell them that something can't be done or that an idea won't work. Passionate leaders keep going and persist in spite of barriers. They make courageous decisions for the good of the cause. They take chances and stick their necks out when no one else will.

Medical Center of the Rockies in Loveland, Colorado, received one of Avatar's Bold, Daring and a Little Gutsy awards for innovation. I think this organization's success is clearly driven by passion for excellence and an unwavering commitment to doing what is right for the patient and the family.

Raising the bar:
Medical Center of the Rockies promotes family-centered care

When the Medical Center of the Rockies (MCR) opened in February 2007, leaders Kay Miller and Debbie Delk saw a unique opportunity to set a new standard of care for their organization. Miller, the vice president and chief nursing officer, and Delk, the director of the emergency department, wanted to make sure that they had a family-centered care model in place. As only the second acute care hospital in the Poudre Valley Health System (PVHS), MCR had the chance to create a unique approach to care. The leaders accomplished this by reaching out to the community to learn what patients identified as the most important factors in their medical care.

The newly-built hospital has 136 beds with an emphasis in trauma and cardiac care. For that reason, the emergency department experience was crucial to the hospital's reputation and, ultimately, its success.

In preparation for the facility's opening, the leaders started by reviewing all procedures and policies from its sister facilities. They examined every process according to the needs of patient and family, as well as the efficiencies created by the processes in place.

So often in health care, we think that we understand what the patients want, only to find out that we are badly off the mark. Not wanting to take that chance, MCR leaders invited community members to participate in focus group to help design the care model in the new emergency department. Eighteen community members came together to discuss their recent ED experiences in other facilities. They shared what it was like to have an unplanned visit to the ED and what would make it better.

"The stories we heard were so touching," says Miller. "The patients could give us the first-hand account of what made their ED visits excellent or barely tolerable. But in every case, their experiences were memorable. No amount of research could have shed as much light on the need for family-centered care as these stories. The patients and family members were so engaged that they opted to stretch the meeting past the original 90 minutes just so that they could share what was most important."

According to Delk, "One theme bubbled up to the top during the focus groups. The whole theme of communication surfaced as one of the most important issues to the patients. That could be communication between the patient and the health care provider or between the staff and the families on site, as well as communication with family members who are not present."

"When the patients told us that communication was so important, we specifically wanted to learn from them what we could do to improve," says Miller.

What resulted from the focus groups was an award-winning emergency department recognized for its spirit of innovation. The department received Avatar's Bold, Daring, and a Little Gutsy award for 2007 for its approach to family-centered care.

"The No. 1 decision was to adopt a policy that placed no restriction on visiting," explains Miller. "Family members can go back to the treatment rooms and even two or three members are acceptable. Imagine having a sick or injured child. All of us said, 'Just try to keep me away from my child.' But changing employees' mindsets isn't always easy. Even though we were opening a new hospital, our staff was coming to us with lots of experience in other organizations. That meant that they had some established opinions and attitudes to overcome. It required work and collaboration. We met with some resistance at first, but like everything else, time helps."

"We actually wrote into job description that the patient decides who their family is," says Delk. "There are many different support systems outside of the traditional, nuclear family. So it only makes sense that the patient be the one to define his or her family. In some cases this concept really stretched staff to think about their preconceived ideas."

During discussions with the community, three themes emerged. Patients and their families:

- Want to be kept informed at all times
- Want to stay together
- Want to know why they are waiting

"We created job performance standards that holds staff accountable for keeping the patient and families informed about why they are waiting," adds Delk. "We do regular rounds and continually check on that. Staff know that they are accountable for keeping patients informed and that (this information) will be included in performance reviews.

"We try to continually check back that we are actually carrying through on what the patients have told us is most important," says Delk. "When rounding in the ED we ask the patient or family member, 'Can you tell me what you are waiting for? Or, do you know what your plan is?' We all do that on rounds so every staff member knows that this is the drill. It is expected and they will be held accountable."

"We had an advantage though," explains Miller. "Because we were hiring all new staff we were able to set that expectation from the very beginning. From the very start, staff knew that they would be rounded on. This way we didn't have to help them adjust to a change. It was just the way we set things up."

MCR has made great strides. It is a rare occurrence to have a patient admitted to the inpatient unit who is complaining and upset about their experience in the emergency department.

"This is (now) a totally different environment," says Delk. "The traditional approach to trauma was to whisk family members off to a quiet room where they would meet with a social worker or nurse dedicated to them. We thought that this was good for them, but in reality it was good for us, not the family. Now, if the family wishes, we bring them right into the trauma room even if the patient is being resuscitated. Of course, we still have a social worker or nurse dedicated to supporting them. We also make sure to tell the team that there is a relative present who wants to come in. We offer this option to the family instead of automatically refusing them access. We have found that it is helpful for the family to see the team working so hard to do everything possible for their loved one."

To further aid communication, the entire facility is wireless. Anyone can use a cell phone without a problem. MCR has also placed phones or phone jacks in the exam rooms and waiting areas in case someone wants to make calls but doesn't have a cell phone. "Families need to stay in contact with one another during a crisis," says Delk. "By making communication easy, we are helping to ease their minds."

Today, MCR has one year's worth of data and is continually looking for opportunities for improvement. "We expect great things and we have exceeded that expectation each month. We monitor constantly, and want to keep on improving," agree Miller and Delk.

The MCR emergency medical director takes scores seriously and shares them with the ED physicians as well, who are also accountable for improving scores.

To keep the goal clear and understandable, MCR focuses on the "top box" or highest score. Today that top box accounts for about 78 percent of all scores, exceeding their original goal of 72 percent. Even though MCR knows that a top box score of 78 percent would place them in top 10th percentile of database, they focus on top box. "It keeps everyone clear on the importance of moving from good to great," says Miller. "In addition, we know that the top box is just easier for our entire work force to understand. A percentile ranking vacillates each month. Now our staff has a clear idea about what we are shooting for. They all understand that number and know exactly what we are trying to change."

Not willing to rest on its laurels, MCR continues in the quest for excellence. The goal of PVHS is to receive the Malcolm Baldrige National Quality Award. At the time of this interview, PVHS has had three site visits. Although the health system has not received the award to date, leaders have taken the lessons learned from the reviewers and applied them in continuous improvements. Among the organization's strategies is a strong focus on engaging the work force toward the MCR's service initiative, including volunteers and medical staff.

What lessons have Miller and Delk learned on their journey? "The biggest 'Ah-ha!' moment for me was seeing that our patients really do know what they want for service," says Miller. "They know what they want when they come to a facility and what experiences will cause them to return. They are clear about what it means to be treated well."

"We know that (a medical facility) can have all the fancy gadgets in the world, but it's what happens - the experience - that makes people want to come back," says Delk. "We have to remember that the experience isn't about us. It's about the patient and family. The more you can focus on that, the more successful patient care will be.

It's collaboration with the patient and family, rather than a prescriptive relationship. We need to continually ask, 'How can we make this an optimal outcome for you?'"

Raising the bar:
CHRISTUS Health guarantees service and continues journey

If I have ever met a health care leader who embodies all five of the essentials covered in this book, it is Dr. Tom Royer of CHRISTUS Health in Irving, Texas. Throughout this book I have featured stories about leaders who excelled at setting priorities, developing people, establishing processes, fostering purpose and leading with passion. But when I met Royer, I found a leader who personifies all of these leadership essentials, with a track record that clearly documents the fruits of his leadership.

Royer is clearly passionate about health care in general, and about the work being done at CHRISTUS in particular. He is quick to recognize that real progress toward excellence takes a strong, focused team that is equally passionate about health care. Dr. Royer defines health care as "a sacred ministry, because people turn their lives over to us. That is a sacred trust that we can never take for granted."

Royer, a surgeon, began his medical career at Geisinger Medical Center in Danville, Pennsylvania, where he assumed a leadership position on the medical staff while still in his residency. Before joining the newly-formed CHRISTUS Health in 1999, Royer held leadership positions with The Johns Hopkins Hospital and Health System as well as Henry Ford Hospital in Detroit.

Royer recalls the day during his residency when he first came face-to-face with his personal mission and sense of purpose. During his rounds with the chief resident, where his task was to make an assessment and then return to the group of residents to report his diagnosis and propose a course of treatment, he walked into a room where a 2-year-old patient was cradled in the arms of her mother. "I introduced myself ... and said I needed to examine her child," Royer says. "(The mother) held the child out to me and I was dumbstruck. This woman was literally placing her most precious gift in my hands - her baby. The magnitude of that responsibility left me reeling."

After the examination, when Royer returned to the residents, he told them he was overwhelmed. The chief resident thought he meant that he didn't understand the child's diagnosis. "I told him I was very clear about the diagnosis and the appropriate treatment," says Royer. "What was overwhelming was that I was in a position now that placed such an enormous responsibility on my shoulders. That was a defining moment for me in my medical career. I knew at that very moment that I could never take for granted the importance of my work in health care. People place their very lives in our hands, and I intended to make this sacred ministry my life's work. I felt that once I assumed that responsibility I had entered the journey of excellence. And that journey is a lifelong journey."

The CHRISTUS journey toward excellence hasn't been an easy one. The system was formed in 1999 after a merger between two Catholic systems based in Houston and San Antonio. The merger and subsequent expansion now includes 30,000 employees and 6,800 physicians, and spans six states in the United States and five states in Mexico. Unifying a culture spanning such a large geographic region and uniting two separate systems was nothing short of daunting. But Royer was committed to do it. One of the first milestones under his leadership was to unite two systems under one common mission, vision and set of core values. Royer knew that in order to align every individual on the journey toward excellence, the first priority was to clearly articulate a new mission and vision.

In 2000, less than one year after the system was formed, the leadership team announced that CHRISTUS Health would be begin a Journey to Excellence with accountability in four distinct, measurable performance categories: Clinical Quality, Service Quality, Business Literacy and Community Value. Specific goals were set under each of the four Directions to Excellence. The priorities were clearly stated and aligned with the mission and vision, and all CHRISTUS facilities were accountable for achieving the specific goals.

The organization made some significant improvements, and received one of Press Ganey's Success Story Awards in 2005 after demonstrating an impressive increase in both associate satisfaction and in patient satisfaction in inpatient and emergency care. "But a journey of excellence means you don't quit, even when you are celebrating successful gains," Royer says, adding that he congratulated the staff on the award but "reminded them that we were still on the journey."

That's when a nurse stood up and asked Royer, "Is it ever enough for you? Will you never be satisfied?" Royer replied, "No." He explained that even if the organization were at the 99th percentile, it would still not be delivering the best to that 1 percent. "Do you want your mother to be the 1 percent in our ED who gets marginal service?" he asked her. "I don't."

Later, the nurse approached Royer and agreed that she could understand his point - "But her questions," he says, "reminded me that we still had a long way to go." For those health care organizations with lower scores, says Royer, "The challenge is ... the energy that it takes to get up from the 60th to the 80th percentile."

Hit the wall or the finish line?

In order to keep building the momentum and passion for excellence, Royer decided to seek role models by consulting two groups of people in his organization that are known for their endurance in the face of adversity - marathon runners and mountain climbers. After he interviewed them, he asked them to speak to the staff. They shared their inspiration to keep moving toward their goals.

The marathon runners talked about "hitting the wall" at the 21st mile and knowing that quitting was not an option - since the triumph comes from crossing the finish line. The mountain climbers discussed the feeling of reaching the height at which oxygen is scarce and physical fatigue and cold make finishing feel impossible - but nevertheless, the climber perseveres until the summit is reached.

The athletes also pointed out that part of their prescription for success was tied to celebrating milestones along the way to keep them pumped up. Each mile for the runner was an opportunity to celebrate and consider how far he'd come. "Their stories were inspirational for all of us, and at the same time, reminded us how important it is to celebrate the milestones," says Royer.

"After listening to their stories of endurance and perseverance, we crafted a motto: 'For us, nothing is impossible.'" Royer feels that this motto has a direct correlation to sustained success. "You have to teach people to love being in a high-performing organization," says Royer. "It just becomes too easy to start being okay with mediocre. You see this in tenured academic positions and in military as well. I can't accept being okay with mediocrity when the very core of our business is human life."

CHRISTUS leaders put vital processes in place to help to sustain progress. Royer says, "Unless we demand excellence, we are breeding mediocrity." To put teeth into this belief, CHRISTUS began offering a service guarantee - with specific promises - to all of their inpatients. Instead of centering the guarantee on perfunctory tokens of apologies if patients weren't satisfied, it was based on three priorities for improving patient satisfaction: curious, prompt, and compassionate care; concern for special needs and privacy; and open, honest communication about treatment.

The service guarantee program includes a process for tracking complaints and initiating rapid-cycle improvement. An employee reward and recognition program was developed to build "Champion Teams" throughout the organization that focus on satisfaction.

CHRISTUS developed "Must-Have" strategies to enhance staff interactions with patients and their families. These include:

- Scripts and key words for patient encounters
- Rounding programs
- Clear expectations and measures of accountability
- Processes for sharing and transferring best practices across facilities through individual meetings with facility satisfaction teams and monthly system-wide team sessions

"Customers today are sophisticated and understand our score-cards better than we once thought," says Royer. "Measurement is how the health care package is wrapped and presented to the con-sumer. We must be accountable to the public for our quality meas-ures."

Royer understands the importance of building a competent and confident leadership team. He engages leaders in what he calls "pro-fessional back-talking." He says, "I want to be challenged. I want people to know that they have a responsibility to voice their opin-ions and push the envelope for the good of the patient. That behav-ior is how we foster innovation and speak on behalf of the patient."

Being a physician himself, Royer has the pedigree and personal experience to challenge the medical staff. "Physicians must remain humble in their approach to people and at the same time demon-strate what I call clinical egotism," says Royer. "We have to be strong decision makers or we couldn't make timely, critical decisions. We need to exude clinical egotism in order to remain confident in clin-ical decisions. This helps us to move quickly and decisively when needed and helps to build patient confidence in us. But at the same time, we cannot let that clinical egotism become arrogance to the point where we alienate others."

At one point in his career, frustrated with poor patient satisfac-tion and determined to engage the medical staff in making improve-ments, Royer took a unique and memorable "performance approach" rather than an academic approach to communicating the patients' perspective. After he had finished presenting satisfaction data at a house-wide medical staff meeting, Royer dimmed the lights on the stage. When the lights came up, only one spotlight lit the stage. That light was aimed at a gowned patient sitting on a gurney.

The gowned 'patient' was Royer, who told the crowd: *"I am your patient. Today, 950 of us will be discharged from this campus. Of those, 450 will tell our friends and neighbors that we have had a poor or mediocre experience. And those friends will tell other friends and so on and so on ... I am your patient. What will you do tomorrow to raise my confidence in you? What will you do tomorrow to make sure that I want to return? What will you do tomorrow to ensure that my experience is the best that it can be?"*

"You could have heard a pin drop, even though there were about 200 physicians in the room," says Royer. "It was time that they all stopped arguing about the data and started to take some action aimed at improvement."

Royer will be the first to admit that CHRISTUS isn't perfect. But he also knows that the journey is about the willingness to set high expectations and to continue to strive to meet them. "I have a soul of excellence," says Royer, "but I know that it takes a great team to accomplish anything in this world. Just as a surgeon is only as good as the scrub nurse, tech, or intern assisting him, we must all continually strive for excellence and remain connected to purpose. For me, my work in health care has aligned my work and my life perfectly. I don't feel like I go to work. My life's work is aligned here. My pursuit of my vision transcends all aspects of my life because the driver is excellence. Excellence is excellence."

There is a saying: "Love what you do and you will never work a day in your life." I think the message here is that aligning your core values with a sense of purpose, catalyzed by passion, is the formula for a joyful and successful life.

I challenge you to make a fearless connection to your passion in life, whatever that may be. Nurture it and bring it forward. And if you bring that passion into your role as a leader, you will be changing the world - one encounter at a time.

Leader reflections

Reflect and journal on the following:
- How well does your work align with your values?
- Identify something you feel passionate about. This can be a local or global issue or cause. What makes you passionate about this?
- Examine how your values are aligned with the things about which you are most passionate.
- Considering the things about which you are most passionate; ask yourself if you are taking actions that align with your values.

Actions
- Identify three behaviors that you feel demonstrate your passion about an issue or cause.
- Ask your closest colleagues to tell you what they think you are most passionate about in your work. Do their answers match your reflections from above? If not, determine what is misaligned.

In conclusion

Whether you have the title of a leader or just the heart of a leader, remember that passion alone won't move you or your organization to greatness.

The success stories I have shared here demonstrate that it is the five elements - priority, people, processes, purpose and passion - which, when combined, create the strongest formula for leadership. None of the organizations featured in this book would have achieved success if their focus were limited to only one of the five leadership elements. Rather, each example demonstrates that is the combination of these elements that generates the greatest success.

Exploring the five elements of this leadership formula reminds me of my college chemistry labs. I would combine all the necessary elements into a beaker - but nothing would happen, until I added the catalyst. Then ... BANG! I'd get the desired result. Passion is the leadership catalyst. When passion is combined with clear priorities; the right processes in place; and the best people with a clear sense of purpose, the result is a wonderful and exciting explosion - like when I added the catalyst to the beaker.

As health care leaders, we are stewards of a vital community asset. I believe each of us has a responsibility to our communities, and the people that we serve, to align our organizations in a manner that will promote a vital culture of healing. We must be able to articulate the priorities. We must put the right people in place who are armed with efficient processes. And we must support those people in developing a strong sense of purpose.

When we, as passionate leaders, have accomplished these things, we will be able to continue rising the bar.

Keep reaching, stretching and growing toward your vision!

Accountability

Culture of accountability, 65

Holding others accountable, 24, 29

Mutual accountability (Liberty Lutheran), 53

Aloi, Susan, 75-80

Angelou, Maya, 57

Avatar International, 107, 146, 187-189

Bacon, Francis, 3

Baird Model for service excellence, 124-134

Baker, Susan Keane, 138

Baptist Health, 186

Barton, Derrick, 68, 73

Beck, Larry, 185-186

Beeson, Stephen C., MD, 104-105

Behavior-based interviewing, 75-78

Bell, Chip, 98, 103, 177, 187

Berrett, Britt, 14-16

Beryl, 8-9

Bliss, Jeanne, 18

Bold, Daring, and a Little Gutsy, 187-189

Brand, xv, 10, 11, 97

promise, xv, 10

Budget, 2, 3, 7, 26, 45

Burdick, Jana, 167-169

Campbell, Michelle, 165-166

Catalyst, 16, 33, 67, 200

Center for Talent Retention, 67-75

Chief Customer Officer, 18

CHRISTUS Health, 175, 193, 198

Churchill, Winston, 176

Coaching

examples of five steps, 90-91

growing people through, 82-832

Coaching cont.

low performers, 108

problem-oriented approach, 92-93

self assessment, 88

"Coaching For Improved Work Performance", Ferdinand F. Fournies, 932

Collins, Jim, 58, 186

Communication

cascading, 39-41

goals, 38

planning grid, 37

team, 131-132

Core competency

related to innovation, 134-137

Covey, Steven, 172

Customer experience, 10

"Customer Loyalty Guaranteed-Create, Lead, and Sustain Remarkable Customer Service", Chip bell & John Patterson, 98, 103

"Customer Service in Health Care", Baird, Kristin, 75

Customer Service Team, 124-136

Davis, Chad, 108

Delk, Debbie, 188-192

Diderot, Denis, 175

Disengaged, 67-71

E to the third power, 13

Eastern Maine Medical Center, 145-148

Employee of the month, 132

Engagement

employee engagement, 67-75

impact of innovation on, 137

Etter, Carl, 46-49

Everett, Beth, MPH, RD, 187

Expectations
  related to moment of truth, 140

Experience mapping, 137-141

Experience mapping worksheets, 139

Fast Company, 116

First impression, 6, 92, 94, 96, 97

Fisher, Luanne, 52-54

Fournies, Ferdinand F., 93

Frankl, Viktor, 152-153

Goals

  clarify, 17

  communicating, 19-22

Gogarty, Shawn, 107-108

Good Samaritan Hospital, 185-186

"Good To Great- Why Some Companies Make the Leap and Others Dont" Collins, Jim, 186

Greenland, Carol, 162-163

Greidanus, Thomas G., 1076-109

Guber, Peter, 35-36

"Hardwiring Excellence", Studer, Quint, 65

Harvard Business Review, 35

HCAHP, *xiii, xv*

HealthLeaders Magazine, 106

"Heroic Checklist - Why You Should Learn to Love Checking Boxes, The", Heath, Dan & Chip, 116

Hinton, Jim, 168

Hiring, 73-80

  for fit, 73-75

Hospital Check-up Report, 58-61

Innovation
  team, 133-134

Innovation Cafe – Memorial Hospital, South Bend, 134-137

Job descriptions, 27-29, 77-81

Job Egg, 164-171

Johns Hopkins University School of Medicine, 116, 193

Kennedy, John F., 151

Kissenger, Henry A., 178

Labelle, James Dr., 48-51

Leader Reflections, 55, 111, 1487, 172, 199

Liberty Lutheran, 52-54, 99

Lipman, Doug, 36

Lloyd, Robin, 118-121

Lombardi, Vince, 82, 89

Luther King Jr., Martin, 176

Machiavelli, Niccolo, 1

"Managing Patient Expectations", Baker, Susan Keane, 138

Marriott, Willard J., 113

McDonald, Jill, 146-148

Measurement Team, 126-131

Medical Center of the Rockies, 188-192

Medical City, 14-16

Memorial Hospital of South Bend, 134-137

"Micromessaging- Why Great Leadership is Beyond Word", Young, Stephen, 42

Miller, Kay, 188-192

Mission,
  in sense of purpose, 159
  in setting priorities, 7-8

Moments of truth, 137-139

Morris, Tom, 22

Mustful, Cindy, 68

Mystery shopping, 10, 12, 62, 95, 106

Neiman Marcus, *xv*

Newbold, Philip, 1354

Nightengale, Florence, 176

"No Asshole Rule, The", Sutton, Robert, 66-67

Nordstrom, *xv*

Organization FIT Interview Process, 73-75

Organizational EGG, 164

Orientation, 6, 40, 53, 78, 96-99, 115, 135, 162

Park Nicollet Health Services, 159-161, 171-173

Parkview Medical Center, 107-109

Patient expectations, 130, 138-141

Patient experience pathway, 139

Patterson, John, 98, 103

Performance appraisals,15-16, 27-28, 78, 126

Physician engagement, 15

Physician Fire Starter, 105

Poudre Valley Health System, 188

"Practice Excellence- A Physician's Manual to Exceptional Health Care", Beeson, Stephen, MD, 104

Presbyterian Healthcare Services, 164, 172,

Press Ganey, 19, 57-59, 192

Priority, 1-55

Priority pyramid, 7, 21, 155

Processes, 112-148

Recognition, 31-33

Recognition Team, 131-132

Reimer, Renee, 164-171

Ridenhour, Christopher, 52-54

Ring, Elliott, 107-109

Ritz-Carlton, 186

Rounding, 190, 196

Royer, Tom, 175, 193-198

SWAT teams, 20, 39, 126-131

Schweitzer, Albert, 43

Scripps Memorial Hospital, Encinitas, 46-51

Script, 61, 196

Sense of purpose, *xii, xviii*, 4, 35, 153-159, 167, 198

Service Excellence Team (SET), 122-134

Service Recovery, 121, 141-144

Service standards, *xii, xiv*, 27, 53, 75, 77, 81, 126, 131, 183

Simmons, Annette, 36, 182-185

Spalla, Deidre, 162

Spiegelman, Paul, 8-10

St. Luke's Episcopal Health System, 74

Stakeholders, 37, 40, 148

Standards, 27-31

Standards Team, 126

Stonemasons, 154-155

Storytelling, 35-36, 97, 133, 182-185

Studer, Quint, *vi*, 65, 167, 178, 186

Suggestion box, 133

Sutton, Robert, 66-67

Talent Performance Model, 73

Transparency, *xi, xv*

Turnover, 2, 9, 21, 62-65

United Technologies Corporation, 4

University of Utah Hospitals and Clinics, 117-121

Values,
   connection to priority, 7-8
   related to sense of purpose, 152-156

Very Good Care Initiative, 145-147

Vigil, Christina, 169-171

Vision
   connection to priority, 7-8

Watley, Denis, 17

Wikipedia, 98

Wow Wizard School, 135

XYZ formula, 92

Young, Stephen, 42

Zachry, Jan, 4